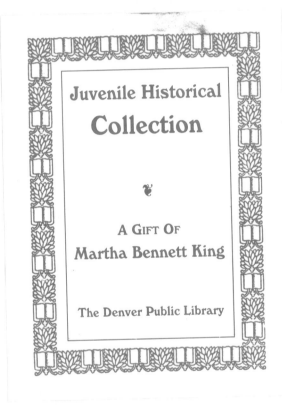

S et in medieval France against a backdrop of castles and barons, tumbled ruins and peasants, here is the wondrous tale of a man who tames the fierce, red-eyed wolf who lunges out of the dark forest in the dead of the night.

The journey ahead of this man named Tegonec and the wolf, christened Roland, is one of hardship, adventure, and amazing discoveries. Together they battle and outwit the knights of the court, they rescue and befriend the orphan boy Triggot, and they speak to each other in a special language of understanding and trust.

The man, the beast, and the boy—a motley trio—travel throughout the land, discouraged by their poverty and beguiled by temptations of wealth and power. Then, in a frightening whirl of pride, selfishness, and betrayal, they are suddenly torn from each other. The road home becomes a desperate search for the peace that will only come to Tegonec, Roland, and Triggot if they can somehow find each other again and rekindle their lost friendship, faith, and love.

Wolf Roland

Also by Julia Cunningham

The Treasure Is the Rose
Burnish Me Bright
Candle Tales
Dorp Dead!
Far in the Day
Macaroon
Onion Journey
Viollet
The Vision of Francois the Fox
Maybe, A Mole
Come to the Edge
A Mouse Called Junction
Flight of the Sparrow

Wolf Roland

by Julia Cunningham

PANTHEON BOOKS
NEW YORK

Library of Congress Cataloging in Publication Data
Cunningham, Julia.   Wolf Roland.
Summary: After losing his beloved donkey to a ravenous wolf,
a poor man is roused to such sorrow and anger that he challenges the beast
to take the place of the donkey and pull the cart that is his livelihood.
[1. Wolves—Fiction. 2. Friendship—Fiction. 3. Middle Ages—Fiction]   I. Title.
PZ7.C9167Wo   1983   [Fic]   82–19068
ISBN 0–394–85892–1   ISBN 0–394–95892–6 (lib. bdg.)

For Mae Durham Roger
with ever-present love

Wolf Roland

CHAPTER ONE

*T*egonec was worried about his donkey. During all the years they had been together, Fanfare had never awakened cranky from his afternoon nap. But today he had. Droop-eared, stirring his hooves in the warm straw but not rising, he lifted his head and stared at his master.

Tegonec stared back, trying to understand the series of small grunts that came from deep within the animal's throat.

Fanfare lay back and closed his eyes.

"I know, old friend," Tegonec said to him. "You are tired

of pulling that cart from market to market, from village to village. The stench from the onions curls my stomach, too. And as for the leeks!"

Tegonec sighed. So much trouble at once. Just yesterday the loads he had hauled from farms to the marketplace in the nearest town had been so light, his pay had bought only enough bread and cheese for today. He knew that he would have to leave his snug little hut and take to the road, to work his rounds where the carrots, beans, and cabbages were more plentiful, where he would be needed to transport the overflow the farmers couldn't pile into their own wagons.

And now, for the very first time since he and Fanfare had lived their years together, the donkey was showing his reluctance to go on. He stroked the soft, gray hair of his friend's neck.

Fanfare's eyes opened and he regarded his master with affection. The man had been good to him, treated him almost as an equal, even if it had been his donkey's lot to do most of the heavy jobs.

Tegonec scratched him behind one ear. "I've seen that the work has been getting harder for you these past months. How would you like to retire?" he asked, forgetting in his fondness for this weary beast that he would go destitute without his help. Where would Fanfare's hay come from, and the usual Sunday treat of carrot-seed cake that the donkey loved so much?

Tegonec shrugged. "Maybe we should both just lie down and wait for the Dark One."

As though Fanfare had understood, he thrust his legs under himself and stood up, shook the straw vigorously from his coat, and nuzzled Tegonec's shoulder.

Laughing with relief to see his companion willing once more, Tegonec gave the donkey a happy slap on the rump. "That's no way for a man to talk, is it? Not one who has journeyed the roads of the world in wind and rain, singing. Remember the night in the dark of the moon when we were wobbling our way through the forest, and me with seventeen francs in my pocket, and suddenly we saw three robbers ahead of us on the path?"

Fanfare's eyes were agleam, responding to the enjoyment in his master's voice.

"And you split their eardrums while I howled like a ghost from hell and they scurried off like rabbits?"

Full of energy no matter how his joints creaked, the donkey brayed and went to stand between the shafts of the rickety little cart that had served them so many years and miles.

"Ho, ho! Ready to go, are you?" Tegonec waved his right arm in the air. "Off to the far reaches of forever!"

Preparations were quickly made. After Fanfare was harnessed, the cart was loaded with what little remained of his fodder, and on top of that two blankets folded and rolled around a bowl, a frying pan, an axe, a flint for making fire, and a tiny square plaque of wood with a blurred saint's face painted on it. Half a loaf of bread and a small square of cheese made a modest parting meal. More must be earned tomorrow.

Tegonec fastened the outer latch of the hut's door—there was nothing inside to steal but a broken-legged stool and a torn curtain—and, glancing up at the sky that was closing down into evening, nodded toward the single star that shone between gathering clouds.

He pulled from the pocket of his ragged jacket a small metal triangle with four strings fastened taut from top to bottom—his harp. He strummed it as he sang:

> *"To and fro,*
> *Fro and to,*
> *Wherever you go*
> *I'll shepherd you."*

Then he carefully replaced it in its hiding place.

"Come," he said. "The wind is rising and we must reach the next village by morning to earn tomorrow's bread." With a last look at his home, a look of remembering, he straddled the donkey, his legs so long they almost scraped the ground, and without further delay the two of them took to the road.

It was just past midnight when they came to the edge of the forest. Tegonec was asleep, his chin bouncing on his chest, and the donkey's plodding was so slow his hooves dragged trails in the dust until, unable to take another step, he came to a halt.

Tegonec jolted awake. "But where are we?" he said.

Fanfare's eyes opened halfway and he slumped against the right shaft of the cart.

"Poor old friend, you're exhausted. I should have let you rest long ago. Well, wherever we are, it's as far as we are going tonight." Tegonec slid from the bowed back. After he had unbuckled the harness straps, he looked into the dim design of black tree trunks leggined by fern and bush. He soon had a tidy little bonfire going and shared its warmth with Fanfare. He knew how his companion's bones must ache.

"How still it is," he murmured to himself, and closed his right hand around the harp. But something—perhaps the intensity of the silence—checked the impulse and he listened instead. Was that a twig cracking behind him, or was there something or someone coming nearer? He gazed toward the night sky to count the stars, as he had been taught to do when he was a child emerging from a nightmare. But the trees and clouds screened them out.

Suddenly he was so lonely he shivered. He had always been lonely, ever since in his first youth his home had been torched by a marauding baron, his father and mother slashed and burned to death. Tegonec had tried for all the years of his growing up to sear out the memories that had been ashed by those flames, and sometimes he escaped them, but tonight, with not even the comfort of a few coins in his pouch, they rushed at him headlong.

He saw his mother stirring the pot that hung above the hearthstone and heard her voice saying, "Tegonec, my little cabbage, you must always be kind to those who love you and those who hate. There is no greater giving." That was when she had given him the little holy image, the saint who had returned his gaze year after year, and told him of her vision that it would exert great power over his destiny.

He smelled again the coarse material of her skirt as he sat on the floor beside her, leaning his head against her leg. The scent was like her geraniums, those red and white blooms she had nurtured so caringly, long ago trampled by the horses of the killers. She herself had been like one of her flowers, her skin so pale, her cheeks so flushed.

With pain, he remembered finding his father's axe in the rubble, after the fires had dwindled and he had climbed down from the tree that had kept him from being discovered—for they would have put him to the sword, too.

The days of his father's teaching returned to him now— how each morning before sunrise the two of them would walk far into the woods to work and each night come back with a load of chopped logs. These were for the great fire-places of the chateau on the hill, a walled, turreted building Tegonec had never seen except from a distance. And some-times his father would bring a surprise from the castle: a lamb bone with shreds of meat still clinging to it, or, once, two meters of purple cloth for his mother, stuff so soft it seemed to melt in his fingers.

Tegonec scrubbed his face with both hands, trying to rub out these memories; and they had just begun to fade when he heard the stirring of some large living thing in the shadows behind him.

CHAPTER TWO

Out of the night two slanted eyes flared red, reflecting the fire. Tall and gaunt, the figure of an animal stood clear of the trees, its head huge, its ears flattened, tail level. A dreadful snarling issued from between white, pointed teeth. A wolf! A great monster of a wolf that seemed to draw into itself the darkness around it and grow even more terrifyingly enormous, like the soul-consuming creatures of childhood nightmares.

Tegonec felt himself shrivel, his substance turn to water.

He would have pitched forward had he not thought of Fanfare. A man did not desert his friends. With that thought some measure of strength flowed back into him.

"No," he said aloud. For an instant he and the wolf stared at each other, eye to eye.

"Wake up, Fanfare! Wake up!" Tegonec shouted to the sleeping donkey. In one swift motion he stepped forward to the fire and, seizing the axe that lay beside it, hurled the weapon at the savage apparition.

The wolf stood unflinchingly as the blade skimmed its head and disappeared into the bushes behind it. Then, with massive deliberation, the creature crouched, its eyes fixed on Fanfare.

The donkey was rousing himself to the desperation of Tegonec's renewed cries, and had nearly gained his feet when the wolf sprang at his throat.

Unmindful of himself, Tegonec grabbed a flaming stick from the fire and, screaming a curse, flung his body into the wild melee of flailing hooves and slashing fangs. He felt his head jerked backward by a blow to his temple. Then total darkness drowned his consciousness.

The fire had long been cold, its ashes scattered by the wind, when Tegonec came groaning to his senses again. His left cheek was crusted, his hair matted with dried blood. The throbbing pain in his head extended to the length of every limb. He burned with fever and then was shaken by chills.

"Fanfare!" he called out in a thirst-cracked voice, and then wept as memory returned and he gazed at the empty shafts of the little cart.

By the dampness of his clothing Tegonec knew that a light rain must have fallen while he lay unconscious on the ground. He pushed himself slowly upright, pausing as he was taken by bouts of dizziness. When he saw that in the earth all about the place he had lain were footprints left by the wolf since it had rained, he was seized by a new kind of chill, and with it a terrible anger and determination.

He shook his fist at the surrounding trees. "You insolent, murdering beast! I'll find you wherever you are. You shall pay dearly for Fanfare. I swear you shall!"

With water that had collected in a nearby hollow log, Tegonec slaked his thirst and washed the blood from his face and hair. His aching head pounded as he walked unsteadily into the nearest stand of trees. He had to pause every five steps and lean against a trunk for support. Once he was certain he heard a rustling of leaves, as of something forcing its way through. He turned quickly, but his eyes blurred in a momentary faintness and he saw nothing. The sound ceased.

"Coward!" he shouted into the silence. "I know you are there. Come out and show yourself!"

But no one responded except an owl or a passing crow.

Each day Tegonec made a wider circle into the forest. On his rounds he gathered barely enough berries, roots, and mushrooms to sustain life. He had little desire for food, as he was still beset by fevers. Sometimes he thought he must have passed through periods of delirium, for he would find himself back beside the cart without recalling how he had arrived there. Yet the image of Fanfare with the wolf at his throat remained constant. He could remember, however dimly, his own voice reaching out among the trees, calling to the wolf, insisting that the creature confront the evil of his act. He saw himself hacking at it, bone and flesh, until only bits of it strewed the earth. And as the days went by he felt with greater and greater certainty that the wolf, stalking just out of sight, was listening.

One morning before he had unrolled himself from his blanket, Tegonec sensed the presence of the wolf so sharply that he expected to see his enemy standing before him when he opened his eyes and sat up. He saw nothing, but the animal was nearby—Tegonec knew it.

He raised his arms into the air, his hands clenched into fists, and yelled, "Come out, you villain of a donkey killer! Face me if you dare!" He waited. Was there a movement behind the green of the berry bush? "Are you afraid of a gray-headed man with no defense but his bare hands and his wrath? Are you such a craven beast, without conscience, without honor, that you cannot look me in the eye? I'll give you one more chance to come forth or be branded forever as a wolf not worthy of the name!"

It was then that Tegonec saw the gray muzzle of the animal show through the branches of the bush, then the pointed ears and the eyes that glittered yellow in the light of day. Deliberately, the wolf stepped from behind its cover and stood before him. Almost as tall as Fanfare at the shoulder, this enormous beast must be like no other in the world.

Tegonec secretly wished he could disappear. The tense power of the animal was like a touch of cold iron to his senses. Instead he returned look for look. There was an attentiveness, almost more akin to curiosity than fierceness, in the wolf's attitude. Was he being summed up or questioned in some way?

Tegonec felt his heart slow as though in rhythm with the wolf's calmness. What could he read in the creature's eyes? What was that dark pit at their center trying to tell him? He seemed at that moment extended beyond himself, as though he and the wolf were meeting not only as opponents but as beings held in the same balance of understanding.

Bemused by this strange sense of interchange, he found a new image replacing his desire to see the wolf torn limb from limb. It seemed to him suddenly far more important that the creature should be made to acknowledge the life he had taken. In fact, to be suitably punished the destroyer must become that which he had destroyed. The justness of this idea seemed so self-apparently right that Tegonec took a step forward without fear or hesitation and, in a voice of absolute assurance, commanded the wolf, "Step between the shafts of my cart."

The wolf, not three feet distant, cocked his head, and Tegonec read a kind of sardonic appraisal in his expression before the wolf obeyed. The animal dropped even the shadow of menace, and his stance, as Tegonec fastened the harness, was one of tentative acceptance.

Each strap and buckle that had to be readjusted to fit the wolf's thin frame reminded Tegonec of the firm, rounded contours of his lost friend and renewed his bitterness. As he gave the last leather an angry jerk, the hair along the wolf's back rose stiffly, and a deep growl came from the animal's throat.

Tegonec drew back in fright. "What kind of madness have I been drawn into?" he stammered. "Allowing this creature to trick me with his pretense of docility while he waits to tear me to pieces at his leisure, just as he did poor Fanfare?"

"I do not intend to harm you," said the wolf in a soothing voice.

Far from being soothed, Tegonec began to tremble. This was no simple forest creature that spoke aloud to him in his own tongue. He could only have been sent by the Devil himself.

"Where is your fine bravery now?" the wolf went on. "You were quick enough with your threats in the forest. Had I thought you a coward, I would not have come to you."

Stung by this taunt, Tegonec composed himself enough to ask, "Why do you offer yourself so meekly in my donkey's place? And why should I trust you after what you have done?"

"I have made a choice," the wolf replied. "As for trust, you will find out if I am trustworthy or not. In the meantime you will learn that I can be a fair kind of donkey." With that, he lowered his head and, letting his ears droop to the side, began to shuffle forward in such a perfect imitation of Fanfare's gait that Tegonec was caught between laughter and tears.

The sun was halfway up. Reminding himself that if he was to eat before nightfall he must find work, Tegonec put his few possessions into the cart and set off toward the highway. The wolf and the cart followed a step or two behind.

Even keeping to a slow pace, Tegonec soon found his small store of strength severely taxed. Now and then he sent a backward glance at the wolf, hoping that the animal would find his new work more tiring than he had bargained for or the harness more galling, and that he would ask for respite. But the wolf seemed content to plod steadily onward, and Tegonec was stubbornly determined not to give in first.

Once in open country under the heat of the noonday sun, Tegonec became increasingly light-headed from hunger and fatigue. Still, he was not displeased by what surely were looks of awe the few travelers they met along the way cast toward him and his strange beast of burden. Some crossed themselves and lowered their heads as if praying. Did they sense themselves in the presence of a miracle?

Tegonec's mind began to drift into a realm it had never ventured to before. Could it be his destiny to tame this wolf, a savage emissary of the Devil, to confer upon him the power of human speech and divine conscience? A peculiar elation brought an inner vision. "Saint Tegonec," he murmured almost aloud. For as long as the breath of a bird, he savored the two words.

The wheels of the cart were rattling across a bridge when Tegonec was startled out of these musings by the wolf's voice. "I am going to have a drink from this stream," the animal said. "And then I think you had better lie down in the shade of the willows before you fall in your tracks."

Tegonec failed to understand the connection, but made a polite bow as if to a superior. He laid a hand on the wolf's neck and edged past the man, urging the animal close to his side so that its head was only partially visible.

Tegonec glanced toward the stove as they followed the mayor into the kitchen. No woman stood over the steaming pots.

The man sighed. "They took her to work in the castle. I always told her she was too good a cook, that someone would steal her away. But," he added more cheerfully, "at least I don't have to listen to her nagging." He inspected the stranger. "My, but you are a scruffy pair. Never seen the like of that animal. What is he?"

"He speaks for himself," said Tegonec enigmatically.

The mayor burst into guffaws of laughter. "Does he now? Well, I won't wait a year to hear what he has to say." He busied himself putting out two bowls, a loaf of bread, and a large square of cheese. Filling the bowls with stew, he motioned Tegonec to a chair.

Tegonec ate rapidly, but before his hunger was gone he stopped and placed what remained in the dish on the floor in front of the wolf.

When the mayor looked surprised, he simply said, "An empty stomach never pulled a full cart," and tore off another piece of bread.

"When do you wish us to move your goods?" Tegonec inquired as he chewed the last bite.

The mayor smiled, and his smile was sly. "Not goods exactly," he said. "And not entirely mine."

"I don't understand," said Tegonec.

"And why should you? But be assured that I am not a thief. You see, the reigning lord is going to collect more taxes tomorrow in the form of coins or whatever can be sold to his profit. So the villagers have entrusted to me their monies, which must be well hidden before sunup."

"How about your own cellar?" questioned Tegonec. He knew the ruthlessness of the landowners, who didn't care if they left whole towns deprived and starving.

"Too obvious. This will be the first place the lord's men ransack. No. I have chosen a burial ground in the marshes a mile from the village. I will lend you my greatcoat, for the wind will make tatters of your worn clothes."

"Not tonight, surely!" exclaimed Tegonec, whose legs were stiff from ankle to hipbone.

"It must be tonight. No one will be about, and the cache must be known only to me." He added hurriedly, seeing Tegonec's puzzlement, "To protect my people, of course. If they are put to the torture, they will have nothing to reveal."

The mayor disappeared to collect the treasure. Tegonec sighed. All he desired at that moment was a layer of straw to lie down on and the hours before morning to sleep through. He felt a nudge against his hand. It was the wolf, and he was shaking his great, gray head.

Tegonec squatted beside him, now on his level. "What is it?" he asked the animal.

"Let us leave, and now" was the wolf's reply.

"And risk freezing before dawn? No. I can't say that I like this man, but if we can be of aid and gain shelter for the night, it would be folly to refuse."

There was a brief flare of resistance in the wolf's eyes that, meeting Tegonec's stare, died. The same feeling that had filled Tegonec before returned, and this time he recognized it as pride. Who else had ever mastered a wolf?

"Come! Come!" said the mayor, grunting as he heaved into the room dragging a wooden trunk. He tossed a ragged coat to Tegonec, who shrugged himself into it. "It's never too soon to start. You take one end and I the other."

In three minutes the chest was loaded into the cart, the wolf once more harnessed; and, the mayor leading, they quietly walked through the silent, shuttered village.

By the time Tegonec, on his knees, had dug into the hardened ground deep enough to lower the trunk into its grave and conceal it, he no longer had the strength to rise but remained on all fours, his head bent.

"No purpose in prayers," said the mayor mockingly.

The wolf strained against the thongs that attached him to the cart and nudged his master. Tegonec's wonderment gave him a spurt of energy, and he looked upward at the wolf. Just as he was about to touch the beast's coarse fur, the wolf lunged sideways, knocking Tegonec to the ground, and leaped high into the air.

A yell from the mayor and a swift turnabout told Tegonec what had happened. As he commanded the wolf to release his jaw hold on the mayor's left leg, he saw the frantic man drop a short, heavy club he had raised against him, intending to crush Tegonec's skull.

The wolf obeyed but held the would-be assassin at bay, his teeth bared, snarls clotting his throat; and as Tegonec got to his feet, it was the mayor who was kneeling.

"Save me! Save me!" he shrieked. "You can take the gold, all of it, but let me go!"

For an instant Tegonec was tempted to let the wolf have his way. He had never before wished the death of any living being, but now he realized that this man had deceived the villagers into stockpiling their gold before the lord's men came to rob them, and that after they had gone he would keep the treasure for himself and no one would be the wiser. He could always lie, saying that the invaders had discovered the money. But to accomplish this, he would have had to get rid of the one witness to the burying.

Tegonec picked up the club and raised it over the mayor's head. For an instant it almost seemed to him that the wolf was instructing him to kill. But as quickly he hurled it into the forest. Such an act of violence would poison the rest of his life.

He told the man to rise and was about to take him prisoner, make him confess to the people of his intention in the morning, when the thundering of hoofbeats broke the silence of the night.

The three looked back toward the village. Tegonec gasped. Scattered fires roared high from the torched houses, and a terrible cacophony of cries and screams rose in the wake of the advancing horsemen.

Tegonec had only time to mutter, "Dear Lord, save us!" before they were surrounded by the rearing, stamping animals.

"Couple of strays," said a man in a silver helmet.

"Maybe they know where the town treasury is," said a second.

"Not likely," replied the first. "Look at that one." He pointed to Tegonec. "A beggar at best."

The mayor had stayed on his knees, trying to shrink as small as possible.

"But see here. He's got a beast that might amuse the court. Seize him."

One of the soldiers drew a large net from behind his saddle and threw it over the wolf. Leaping and twisting, the animal tried to wrest his way out of the tangle, but the ropes only bound him tighter as they twined around his legs.

"Muzzle him!"

It took five of them to hold the frenzied wolf before the muzzle was secured. They then lifted off the net.

"You cannot take my wolf!" Tegonec shouted.

"Poor profits this night," said the leader, ignoring the man in front of him. "Let us be off."

The wolf braced his legs against the pull of the rope, but even his great strength could not halt his being dragged like a sack after the horseman.

"I'll come for you. I swear I will!" Tegonec called after

him. He no longer cared about sleep or food or any of the comforts he had so coveted just a few moments earlier. But first he must see that the gold was returned to the villagers. He challenged the mayor. "You will now join with me in digging up the trunk. Then you will give back to the rightful owners what you intended to steal."

"And if I refuse?" said the mayor, no longer threatened by the wolf.

"If you refuse, I shall testify to your villainy in the presence of the people. They will soon obtain justice, and with little gentleness."

The mayor did as he was told, seeing no other means of preserving his reputation, and soon the two of them were on their way back to the village.

Their return to the town was a sad one. Half of the houses had been fired, the pigs taken, and what had once been proud vegetable gardens trampled. The people were busy gathering up the homeless, and the crying had quieted to a buzz of complaints. But when they saw the mayor hauling a cart that held a trunk, they responded to his instructions to group together.

In a very short time the money was redistributed, the mayor hailed as a hero, and the street emptied.

The mayor, whose house had not been harmed, let himself in and with one baleful glance at Tegonec slammed the door in his face.

All alone in the moonlight, the air acrid with smoke, the shutters of every window latched, Tegonec crawled into the cart and mourned the loss of the wolf. What would happen now? First Fanfare—two tears brimmed in his tiredness— now the wolf. How could he live without someone to pull his cart? Perhaps he would have to sell himself to a farmer for the years to come. He stretched out onto the hard boards, his legs dangling over the edge, and waited for sleep.

CHAPTER FOUR

Dawn found Tegonec limping down a long, straight road bordered with elms. He was pulling the cart himself. He tapped each trunk on the left side with his knuckles, as if to leave a sign that the wolf could follow. He was aware of his own idiocy, but this little gesture warmed him. He scoffed at his arrogance of yesterday, at his belief that his dominion over a wolf was an indication of superior power.

A flock of sheep followed by their shepherd bumped him toward the ditch beside the road.

"Watch where you're going," he said crossly to the shepherd.

The man grinned. "Seems to me you're outnumbered," he countered. "A patch of wool from my youngest lamb is worth more than you and your belongings put together. Look at yourself in the next puddle if you doubt me."

Tegonec recovered his manners. "That may be," he said, "but could you tell me if there is a castle nearby where they hold court?"

At this the shepherd let out such a gust of laughter, it set him to sneezing. He wiped his nose on his sleeve and replied, "For all the good it will do you, yes. Just over the next hill. But if I were you, I'd stay out of their way. They're a very mean bunch. Oh, they dress in velvet and dangle gold chains around their necks, but they take what they want with a club in one hand and a knife in the other."

"I must go there," said Tegonec. "They stole my wolf."

Hearing this, the shepherd urged his flock forward, muttering to himself as he went. "Crazy—the roads are full of them these days." He did not look back.

Over the next rise the castle appeared, squat, of dark stone, with stunted towers. Tegonec walked through the tall grasses, around the moat, to the back gate. It had been opened to allow entry to a pack of hunting dogs. He slipped in just behind the Master of the Hounds. He approached the kitchens.

A man in a butcher's apron called to him. "Out the way you came! No room for beggars here."

"I beg for nothing," said Tegonec. "I ask for work."

The man spat at the heap of refuse that cluttered the rear entrance. "Get rid of this stench and I'll sit you down to a meal." He ordered a boy as scrawny as a crow to fetch a shovel, and soon Tegonec was transferring the discolored mass of garbage to a deep hole in the corner of the courtyard. Yet when he had finished, he did not report to the butcher but waited until the first kitchen was empty and then hurried through to the next. He was blocked for a moment by two cooks drinking from a wine bladder. However, they simply accepted him as an assistant and went on talking.

"The baron ordered the banquet for nine tonight. That means they'll be too drunk to taste the guinea hens. Let's keep them for ourselves. Agreed?"

The other nodded.

Tegonec did not delay, but walked with a semblance of confidence through the next room, where the bread was baking, and on into the interior of the fortress.

So many servants and squires and pages were hurrying through the rooms and corridors preparing for the banquet, that Tegonec was merely another unidentified form and no one challenged his presence. Glancing into one of the bedchambers, he noticed a long, purple cloak flung over a chair. What better disguise to cover his shabbiness? He wrapped himself inside it and for the rest of the afternoon mingled with the others, careful not to speak lest they find him a stranger, and always searching for the wolf.

That night no one noticed the tall, purple shadow stationed in a recess at the rear of the banquet hall. He had even been lucky enough to reach the hunks of fowl cast off by the diners, and once he picked up a large bone with meat still hanging from it. This he tucked into his belt for future eating.

But where was the wolf? He had even explored the stables and the kennels. Just as he had decided to give up and leave this huge hall filled with shouting, drinking, and gorging, two armed guards appeared in the doorway just behind the baron's table. With them was the wolf, held securely by a leather noose set with barbs on the inside so that the least movement gave him pain. The animal's head was down, his body lax.

The baron ordered them to stand before him. "A fine creature, indeed," he said. Then, the grease from his chin running down into his beard, "But what can he do to entertain me?"

One of the guards yanked the noose. "He can sing, milord."

The wolf yelped.

The baron's lady raised her right hand impatiently. "This does not amuse me. Set the hounds on him for sport, if you like, but let's have the troubadors in."

But before anyone could obey her, the wolf—now pricked into anger—slashed at the arms of his captors, freeing himself. He stood, huge with rage, before the baron, his teeth showing.

"For the sake of all that's holy," yelled the baron, "kill him!"

At that instant Tegonec stepped from his hiding place and strode into the center of the hall. "Wait!" he called up to the nobles. "I can tame the beast with my harp."

The baron, cowering low in his seat behind the thick oaken table, said, "Do what you can, but hurry or we shall all be bloodied!"

Tegonec pulled the little stringed triangle from his pocket and began to pick out a tune, his left foot tapping to the tempo of it. Under cover of the sound he spoke to the wolf, scarcely moving his lips. "Pretend now as you've never pretended in all your life. Pretend to be tame or we're lost!"

The wolf's eyes showed consent and he began to lessen the volume of his growling until it was no more than a deep rumble. The courtiers gasped at this show of magic. But when the wolf fell to his knees before the baron and his lady, their amazement changed to applause and excited laughter.

Tegonec knew he could not hold them much longer. He slipped the barbed noose from the wolf's neck and, without haste, turned his back on the nobles and began to walk toward the rear entry.

The baron called out, "Seize the wolf. I'll have him for my pet. Reward the minstrel and send him off."

Tegonec whispered to the wolf, "Be fierce again. Quickly!"

The wolf raised his head and howled with such force, many of the courtiers stopped up their ears. The guards fell back, and now on the run, Tegonec and the wolf raced to the doorway.

Through the courtyard and out the main gate they went,

with such swiftness the peasants feasting outside were ever after unsure of just what they had seen.

When they reached the cart, Tegonec gestured to the wolf to get inside and then flung his cape over him. He put himself between the shafts, and off they sped down the road.

*W*hen they had stretched the distance so far that the castle was no longer visible, Tegonec dropped the shafts and sank to the ground. For several moments he breathed in shudders. The wolf had climbed from the cart and was seated only a yard from Tegonec, gazing at him intently.

Tegonec realized as he met the animal's look that something needed to be said. "What is it?" he asked.

"I must exercise my nature," said the wolf solemnly.

"You mean you don't wish to pull my cart?"

"That is part of it," responded the wolf. "But not all. If I am cut off from my wildness, I shall sicken. Listen while I tell you of my past."

Tegonec settled himself against a tree trunk.

"Many were the nights when I would measure my journeys by the rising and descending of the moon, journeys without pause at a straight run. I was the wind of winter, the flight of the sky-strung geese. I was the river, the sweep of the scythe through wheat. I skimmed the flat of the meadow, across the marshlands, over the very curve of the earth, a shadow too swift for seeing. I was the leader of my pack, until I was injured and they had to choose another."

The wolf paused, but Tegonec continued to listen.

"Even alone as I am now, I must not be deprived of my nature. That is why I cannot promise you true fealty."

Tegonec frowned. "But you owe it to me." The image of the donkey filled his mind, and then the old pride returned to him that he, a simple peasant, could tame a wolf. Who else in all history had achieved such a miracle? He searched for a reply, one that would bind his beast to him forever.

"Perhaps if you were christened, you would lose this wildness." An unwelcome warmth that was like a fever tingled his skin and his stomach tightened. He drew out the meat bone he had picked up at the castle and offered it to the wolf, but the wolf shook his head.

"I am not hungry for that," the animal said. He looked directly into the man's eyes "But I guess having a name wouldn't make me any less a wolf."

Tegonec got to his feet and scanned the horizon. As though it were a prayer granted, he saw the domed outline of a chapel against the star-filled sky.

"But look!" he cried. "The forefinger of the hand of God has shown itself! Come. We will go there and have you christened."

His hope to divert the wolf from his yearning to be free glimmered alive. "Are you willing to be harnessed just once more? I am so truly tired."

The wolf stepped between the shafts and stood very still while Tegonec fastened the straps. As they started for the building, Tegonec was greatly cheered, though the ache in his joints slowed his footsteps.

When Tegonec pulled the bell rope that hung at the side of the high, wooden gate, he glimpsed the eyes of the porter through the spy hole. There was caution in his stare.

"May we come in?" Tegonec asked. A sudden breath of cold wind whirled around the stone wall, and he coughed from the chill of it.

"Who are you?" demanded the porter.

"Just a traveler, asking shelter."

The gate opened, but not wide enough to permit Tegonec to pass through. "You look too poor to wish us harm"—he noticed Tegonec's pallor—"too weak to fear." He swung the gate wide. "Come in."

But as Tegonec led the wolf and the cart into the enclosure, the porter, a small man but sturdy, tried to shove him backward. Tegonec stumbled and fell. The man hastened to lift him to his feet.

"I am sorry," he said, "but your beast frightened me. Are you hurt?"

Tegonec rubbed the soreness of his ribs. "Only a little. Will you give us welcome?"

"You certainly," said the porter, trying to make up for his harshness. "But not that savage animal tied to your cart."

Tegonec wanted to explain how he had tamed the wolf, weave a proud story that would be repeated to the monks until it became a legend, but he was too exhausted. "Not even in the name of St. Francis, who loved all beings?" he asked gently.

A flush of shame reddened the porter's cheeks. "Wait here. I will consult with the abbot." He scurried toward the cluster of gray stone buildings that encircled the chapel, and vanished into one of them.

"Now," said Tegonec with his last thrust of strength, "this is our chance." He hastily unknotted the thongs and, gripping the wolf by the scruff of his neck, pulled him across the cobblestones and through the swinging doors of the chapel.

Once they were inside, all haste fell away. They were enveloped by a fragrant darkness, illumined only by five lighted candles before the altar. The wolf sat down on the paved floor in the center aisle and gazed upward at the figure of a man with his arms outstretched and his face smiling.

Tegonec went down on one knee and crossed himself. He knew they mustn't linger, and turned to the wolf. "Have you chosen a name?"

But the animal remained as if in a trance. Not even his tail stirred.

Tegonec sighed. "Then I must make the choice for you. I hereby give a noble name and christen you Roland."

Just as he finished his pronouncement, he heard a clang of metal as though someone had lifted the latch of a door nearby. "Quick!" he commanded Roland, and was halfway across the courtyard when the porter called to him. "Halt! I have a message for you!"

Tegonec was so short of breath as he reached the outer gate, he thought his heart would pound its way out of his chest. He wrenched the gate open and was about to stagger through when he crumpled to the ground. The wolf stood free.

He paused in front of his master and spoke, only for him: "Roland bids you farewell"—and with that he leaped high and away.

CHAPTER SIX

Each day for two weeks Tegonec awoke to a round of gentle snores, simple but hearty meals, and then again sleep from dark to daylight. His fatigue was soon unremembered. He particularly enjoyed weeding the extensive vegetable gardens, but sometimes, as he pulled up a long-rooted intruder, he wished for the days of past affections. He wished for his mother, always waiting in the doorway when he returned from his daily duties, for his father ready with praise for work well done. He wished himself back on the road, and for Fanfare pulling the little cart filled to overflowing with apples or turnips or onions. And then these images gave place to the wolf, the thieving mayor, the escape from the castle, the christening of Roland, and now —now where was he and where was he going? He remained silent when spoken to, which pleased the monks, since they were bound to have no speech unless urgent.

But one day Tegonec, summoned by the abbot, was met with a difficult question.

"Are you not happy?" asked the broad man, seated in a chair built for two. "Would you not like to join our brotherhood, become one of us? You work well and earnestly and keep to yourself."

"No," replied Tegonec, the single word seeming to speak the whole of what he was feeling.

"But why not?" persisted the abbot.

"I will tell you," said Tegonec, after a small silence. So he did. He recounted the beginning of his journey with Fanfare, the attack of the wolf, and then his chastisement of the beast and the beast's resultant servitude. Here he stopped.

The abbot looked at this simple man benignly. He had heard many tales of man conversing with the creatures of the land and air, and to him that was exactly what they were— tales told by the hearth fire to warm a long evening. And now here was another. "So," he continued, "for the sake of a wolf you must leave? Do you suppose he needs you, a creature of the wild?"

"Perhaps not," said Tegonec, "but I need him."

"To draw your cart? But you could earn an animal, another

donkey perhaps, to do that for you if you worked hard and long enough."

Tegonec did not word his true thought, that he needed Roland in order to fulfill his destiny. The knot of pride was strong within him. Maybe someday this same abbot would place him, Tegonec, among the holy men.

When the monks had assembled to bid him good-bye, Tegonec waved to each one, bowed to the abbot, and, himself harnessed to the cart, took to the road again.

Within the next hour he had the good luck to find a farmer whose wife was ill and who needed someone to take their cabbages to the nearest market town. He had at first scanned Tegonec's shabby appearance doubtfully. "How do I know you will return with my profits?" he asked aloud.

Tegonec smiled. "I will leave my harp in your care."

The farmer turned it about in his hands. "What use have I for such a thing? The voice of my cow is music enough for me."

"You could sell it for two gold pieces," said Tegonec.

The farmer plucked the strings brusquely. The sound started his chickens to cackling. He laughed. "Well, I'll take the chance. Now be off so's to get the first customers, and be sure to boast loudly of my goods."

Tegonec bent forward in the harness and rolled away as fast as the weight of the piled cabbages would allow. He determined to think of neither Fanfare nor Roland, though the straps were chafing his shoulders and his feet burned from the pebbled road. He had chosen to leave the routined existence of the monastery and, mistaken or not, he must make the best of the present.

When he arrived at the market, the sight of the more than one hundred stalls, packed with fruits and vegetables and flowers, with meat and clothing and tools, halted him abruptly. This was a city of sellers. He wondered where he could squeeze in himself and his cabbages.

He had not long to wait to be noticed. A gang of six boys had spied him. "Look at that!" mocked one of them. "A donkey without ears!" Another seized a cabbage and tossed it back and forth to his comrades. "Let's run him off!" said a third, picking up a handful of manure and splattering Tegonec's trousers.

At this moment a very stout woman with arms like pumpkins brandished a cane over the boys' heads. "I'll not miss the next time!" she yelled at them. "You leave this poor man alone." The cane swished nearer and nearer as she advanced upon them. They scattered, laughing.

"Come," she continued, "you can put your cart to one side of my stall and sell from there. You're a brave soul to be tugging that load, and not so young as you might be."

Tegonec thanked her for her kindness and wished he might return it, but the woman was now hawking her own wares, waving her arms for the attention of the passersby, and soon he, too, was beginning to sell.

By noon half of the cabbages were sold, and Tegonec's stomach was announcing his hunger. He began to gnaw on a cabbage leaf, but the woman who had befriended him flipped it from his fingers and cut a thick slice of bread from the loaf under her armpit. "I've not so little I can't also offer you a glass of wine to moisten your bread as well," she said, and filled a cracked mug from a small barrel.

Tegonec ate and drank gratefully as he listened to the woman's chatter. "You never know these days what's going to happen next," she said between mouthfuls. "I mean there's the terrible thieving on every side, and now the Prowler." She wiped her lips on a corner of her smock.

"The Prowler?" Tegonec asked politely, though he really didn't care. It was enough to have something to eat and a job to do.

"You mean you haven't heard? Must be a stranger. Yes—a great, gray beast. Some say it's the Devil."

A flutter of excitement brushed Tegonec's ribs. "What does it look like? Have you seen it?"

She crossed herself. "No, thanks be to the Lord. But my neighbor lost two chickens, and he said it was no fox he saw dragging those hens into the darkness. More like a monster on four legs." She paused to help a little girl choose an apple. "Got eyes that flash red, too, he said."

Tegonec remembered his own first glimpse of the wolf and his heart leaped. "It must be my wolf!" he exclaimed. "My Roland!"

The coins in the woman's hand dropped to the ground. "Mary and Joseph!" she cried. "Here I am next to a madman!" She got up and, pushing Tegonec's cart so that it almost toppled, managed to dislodge it from its space. "Now you get yourself off! Your wolf—even has a Christian name! Maybe you're the Devil." Her alarm mounted. She called to the women in the stalls on either side of her. "Did you hear what this loony just told me?" She repeated Tegonec's words. Five people gathered, then ten, and the talk circled like angry bees.

"Who is he?"

"Where did he come from?"

"His wolf?"

"Better call the guards!"

Tegonec sensed the growing threat, and had just lifted the cart's harness when the first rock hit him. Someone dumped the few remaining cabbages. Another kicked him in the shins, while two more struck at the backs of his knees, making him drop on all fours.

"Look at him now!" the stall woman shouted, a certain glee in her tone. "No better than a dog."

"Or a wolf," added another.

A blow to his head blurred the hovering figures around him, and he was now despairing of ever freeing himself from this whirl of hate when a sound like the howling of the souls in hell issued from the center of the market.

For a moment every motion was cut short in shock. Then, to Tegonec's astonishment, the people dashed in all directions like mice before a cat. The howling had changed to a series of snarls that seemed to choke the air.

Tegonec rose painfully to his feet and looked toward this

sounding dread. Sudden joy lighted his face. Roland—Roland come to save him!

Quickly he hauled the cart out through the throng of bumbling, scrambling people, and as he and the wolf left the square, dragging the cart, and headed for the high road, Tegonec's laughter, though thin with hysteria, was real. In Roland's mouth was a fat leg of lamb.

Once well out of sight of the town, Tegonec stopped to rest. "I am glad to see you," he said rather tentatively, because now he had begun to wonder if Roland had truly come to rescue him or if it was the meat that had brought him into the marketplace.

"And I you," said the wolf.

The silence that followed was not easy. Tegonec glanced toward the empty cart. Should he exercise his power over the wolf and order him to take up his duty? Or should he give in just this once and undertake the menial task himself, but only as far as the farmer's house? What of gratitude?

Slowly Tegonec gripped the ropes of the harness and began to pull. The wolf slouched along behind him.

Roland stayed out of sight as, ten minutes later, Tegonec poured the coins he had earned into the farmer's hands. The man was not displeased by this return, and since he asked for no details of the day, Tegonec gave him none.

Not until the farmer had gone inside his house and shut the door on them did Roland approach his master. Without a word, his eyes as silent as his tongue, he placed himself between the shafts of the cart and waited.

CHAPTER SEVEN

*T*wo days later, the provisions bought by his earn-
ings eaten, with Roland—ears lopped, head and
tail down imitating a donkey's—at his side, Tegonec stood on
the loading platform of a winery waiting to speak to a giant-
sized man who seemed to be the foreman.

He never had a chance even to voice his request for work
before the man leaned over him and, his spittle flecking Tegonec's face, said, "I've plenty of people to do my business.

Now get off this property." He aimed a kick at Roland. "Damned ugly beast you have there. A pair of beggars, both of you! Got no use for such."

Tegonec was about to protest this insult when a stout woman encased in silk came up to them. "But I have," she said, her voice so hollow it seemed to rise from her stomach. She smiled with a curl of her mouth that might also have been a sneer.

Roland shifted his forepaws restlessly and gave her a sidelong glance.

The foreman's meanness dissolved into syrup. "Well, you ought to know what you want, Madame Grue," he said. "You have the responsibility of all those orphans. The city is grateful to you for keeping our streets free of the little scoundrels."

"Come," instructed the woman, quite ignoring the foreman. She led the way down three streets and up one to a two-story block house of gray stone. Instead of entering by the front door, she proceeded to the back, past a bare yard centered by one dead tree. Here they left the cart.

As they passed through two vast storerooms filled with boxes and bins and barrels and lumpy sacks of onions and apples, she spoke again. "The good citizens contribute a certain percentage of their monthly yield to the orphans."

"Then by the quantity, you must superintend a great many of them," said Tegonec to be agreeable. He had noticed that all the windows were barred.

"About ten at the moment," she replied. "The number

varies. Orphans tend not to live very long, you know, though I do keep them confined for reasons of health."

Tegonec wondered whose health she meant.

As though divining his thought, she continued. "That way they can't contaminate the citizens of the town."

Hearing no sound from anywhere as they entered the enormous kitchen, Tegonec asked, "Where are they now—the children?"

There was an abrupt change in the woman's attitude. She lanced Tegonec with very sharp eyes. "One thing is to be understood and right now," she commanded.

Tegonec saw that Roland had not entered the kitchen but was poised in the doorway as if ready to retreat.

"No questions. Just obedience. That is what I require of the children and now of you."

Tegonec sighed and wished for an instant that he was out in the streets, no matter what woe or weather.

The woman suddenly shifted to her former cordiality. "But you must be hungry, dear man." She gestured toward the open cupboards that were filled to capacity. "Help yourself, and your beast, too. Then we will talk business." She left the room.

Tegonec began to cut two thick slices from the long loaf of bread when there was a sneeze in the doorway. He and Roland turned to see a tiny person, no higher than Roland's ears, his face wizened and his body stick thin. He darted across to the counter where Tegonec was standing and snatched the bread from his hand. He crammed it into his mouth until his cheeks bulged.

"Who are you, little one?" asked Tegonec, distressed by this evidence of extreme hunger.

"My name is Triggot and I think myself to be aged nine, sir," said this odd person, swallowing the bread in lumps.

Then, quick as a dragonfly, just as Tegonec was handing a slice to the wolf, he captured this second piece.

Roland opened his jaws wide, but it was only to yawn; and to Tegonec's surprise he didn't even growl.

The child stared into the wolf's eyes as he ate and then he smiled. Roland licked his hand lightly.

Tegonec felt a twinge of jealousy. This was his wolf and his alone. Didn't they share the miracle of speech together as had no other man and beast? But just as he was preparing to order this peculiar being out, the child spoke. "You shouldn't have come," he said, so seriously his forehead crinkled. "No one does well here. There were fifteen of us only a month ago and now"—he shrugged—"eleven going on ten."

"What does that mean, 'going on ten'?"

"By tomorrow there may be only ten of us."

"How is that?"

"Jasper has pneumonia." He looked so sad, Roland went to him and leaned against his side.

"And Madame Grue hasn't called in a doctor?" Tegonec had forgotten his instant of resentment. If all the other orphans were as miserable-looking as this one, they must indeed be ready to exchange their cots for coffins.

Triggot laughed somewhat bitterly. "Oh, it's always too late for potions for the likes of us."

"But why do you stay? Surely it would be less painful to walk the roads even if the ending were the same."

"Haven't you noticed the bars on every window and the locks on all the doors? Only sometimes can an old bar be pried loose. I haven't seen the inside of the town since I was brought here."

"Prisoners," murmured Tegonec.

At that moment footsteps approached from down the corridor. Triggot dived into the storeroom as Madame Grue stomped in.

Her eyebrows rose when she saw how little had been eaten. "No appetite? Well, perhaps that will change after you have accomplished your tasks. You will do my shopping and clean all the rooms."

"In exchange for—?" asked Tegonec, reluctant to agree to anything this hard-shelled woman might suggest.

"For twenty francs a week. I see you are wondering why so much. I will tell you. I do not wish to have any connection with the townspeople except that they pay me, and promptly, for taking the custody of their tag ends of children. You will transact all my business." The statement was flat, as if an agreement had already been reached. "In addition, that animal must be tethered."

Tegonec hesitated. Then he saw again the shrunken visage of Triggot, a face made monkeylike by deprivation, and he nodded at Madame Grue. Maybe he could help, he and Roland together.

CHAPTER EIGHT

*B*ut a week later Tegonec's desire to be of some assistance to the children had thinned. No matter what long hours he spent trying to rid the rooms of filth, the grime seemed a permanent stain, and dust that nothing would dislodge had hardened in the corners and cracks. Roaches held festivals in the kitchen at night, swarms that shimmered, their shiny brown backs clicking against each other, a moving carpet. The rats were bolder and peered at Tegonec as he peeled the turnips or sliced the onions for the daily soup. He always sat in the center of the kitchen, so that he could see them clearly in case they crept too near. Then Roland would force them back into the shadows.

But worst of all were the children. None of them was free of infected sores, and their joints were knobby. Hunger had made caricatures of them. They talked almost not at all, except for Triggot, and then only in whispers, afraid Madame Grue might beat them for a careless word. Even Tegonec began to lose weight at the sight of them around the long kitchen table. His appetite diminished as he watched some of them gulp what was given until they choked, or the others, their stomachs swollen, unable to digest even the small portions in front of them.

One thing, he discovered, did seem to give them some pleasure, and that was Roland. Each evening after he had served Madame Grue her special meal in her chambers, he released Roland into the loft where the boys slept, and sometimes he was even able to hear smothered laughter coming from that top floor.

At first they ventured no more than patting the willing wolf, then stroking his back, but now he played games with them and became their true comrade.

But even this small bright hour in their dark days was not to last.

On Tegonec and Roland's first Sunday at the home, Madame Grue ordered them to assemble all the children in the front parlor. When only six could be found, she exploded. "What is this I see? Last Sunday there were eleven!"

She crossed her club-sized arms and waited, relishing the fear in their eyes.

Then Triggot spoke up. "Madame, if you remember, two died last Wednesday."

For an instant she looked flustered and, glancing at Tegonec, her cheeks reddened. "Oh, yes. Well, that still doesn't account for three."

"I think they ran off," said Triggot.

Her anger returned. "Ran off? Ran off?" She turned on Tegonec. "And how did that happen? You were left in charge. Answer me!"

"I was not hired to be a guard, madame" was Tegonec's reply. In all truth he hadn't noticed the absence of the five. There were so many sick, pinned to their beds by disease and weakness.

She admitted the justice of this by attacking Triggot. "And you? You let them escape—helped them most likely." She slapped him hard across the face, but Triggot did not cry out. She seized his wrist and squeezed. This time he trembled but still made no sound.

Tegonec grabbed the boy by his shoulders and wrenched him out of the woman's grip. Triggot leaned against him, shivering. "That's enough," said Tegonec. "They're gone and that's that."

Madame Grue calmed. "There is only one solution. We shall simply get some more."

"Get some more?" repeated Tegonec.

"You are a very stupid man. How do you imagine I live?

By the head, of course—so much for each from the town council. So all that is required is to go fill the number to ten again."

"You mean apply for more orphans?"

"Apply?" she chortled. "No need for that. Just gather them up off the streets. Their mothers will be grateful to lose them and will believe they just disappeared. Actually"—she paused to smile such a terrible smile that even Roland was momentarily cowed—"actually I'm doing everyone a favor."

Tegonec held Triggot close. This woman must be stopped.

"We'll scour the slums tonight, after dark," she said. "They're easy to find then, on back stoops and in corners that keep off the wind." She left the room, throwing her last words back at them. "Nine o'clock sharp."

When he was certain she was out of earshot, Tegonec sat down on the horsehair couch and drew Triggot beside him. Roland lay at their feet, looking up.

"We must get the others out," said Tegonec.

"And before nine," added Triggot. "Or you will have to help her."

"Can you round them up after supper? Roland and I will meet you with the cart on the back road."

"I can do it," said Triggot, and he flicked his fingers with delight.

"But why didn't you leave long ago, Triggot? You are quick-witted and spry."

Triggot looked embarrassed. "Well, to be quite honest," he said, "I couldn't desert the others, and I had no way to manage their freedom. But now"—he glanced at Tegonec and Roland—"now we are a band." He paused, a wash of doubt blanching his face. "We are, aren't we?"

"We are," said Tegonec. "A band of brothers."

A few hours later, the watered soup eaten and the bowls washed, Triggot climbed the three flights of stairs to the dormitory. He had already alerted the five boys to the plan, but when he entered expecting readiness, two of them were lying on their cots as if struck down.

"What is it?" said Triggot. "We haven't much time, you know. It is close on nine now!"

"They've got something," said one of the standing boys.

"Well, they'll just have to bring it with them, whatever it is. Hurry now. Help them up and get them downstairs if you have to drag them by their ears." Triggot had made his voice stern. They were so used to being ordered about, he knew it would take away some of the strangeness for them.

Somehow, stumbling, clutching one another, Triggot in the lead, they conquered the stairs. But just as they reached the bottom step, one of the sick boys tripped and fell. A squeal of pain cracked the silence.

Hardly breathing, they listened, praying they would not hear the heavy tread of Madame Grue coming to get them. A husky cough came from the next room. On tiptoe with excitement Triggot held up his hands, his fingers crossed. The cough was not repeated and no door opened. Triggot nodded to his comrades and let them out by the back door that Tegonec had previously unlocked. They reached the road just as Tegonec and Roland arrived with the cart. The boys shoved the two weakest ones onto the worn boards, and they set off without a sound into the country of the night.

An hour had passed, and the former silence was now disturbed by sniffles from one of the boys in the cart and sighs by another. Roland had long since requested the aid of Tegonec, and Triggot also gripped one of the shafts of the cart and pulled. Every once in a while Triggot had to lash out at a straggler, though he too felt an ache in his legs and a shortness of breath.

Tegonec called a halt. "We'll take a rest now," he said.

But they had no sooner stretched out on the ground when they heard hoofbeats behind them. Perhaps their absence had been reported.

"God help us!" Tegonec muttered. Then in a loud voice, "Everyone make for the woods. Hurry!"

They scrambled off the road and, with some pushing, some pulling, dived into the cover of the low pines. And none too soon. The troop of horses came so close, the dust from their passing hooves speckled their cheeks. And not until the pounding rhythm had given over to the smaller sounds of the night did Tegonec dare to speak. "We can't return to the highway. So it's the forest for us. The way will be rough, but we have no other choice."

There were a few grumbles from the cluster of boys, and it was Triggot who shamed them to silence. "Would you rather be back with Madame Grue, maybe dying tomorrow

under a blanket full of holes and no one caring?" he challenged. "Here we have a chance, and best of all, we are free."

"Come," urged Tegonec, and he led the group, one hand
on the shaft of the cart, deeper into the dimness of the
forest, Roland shepherding them from behind.

They walked, struggling against roots and vines, lurching
into hollows, half falling and hoisted upright again by their
nearest comrades, until even Tegonec felt himself to be at the
end of his effort.

But just as he opened his mouth to halt them, his feet
encountered a softness that he recognized as grass. He looked
ahead. Far, far off in a dome of moonlight was a clearing,
and in its center rose a low spread of ruins.

"This is a hunting alley," he said. "And see, all of you—
at the end of it our shelter!"

Roland howled with relief, and the boys, laughing feebly,
howled with him. Cheerful now, they trudged toward this
promise of rest.

CHAPTER NINE

The sky was fading into morning when they finally reached the outskirts of the extensive space that had once been the chateau gardens. Now the outlines of the hedges were blurred by overgrowth, and only a few scraggly blooms had survived amid the tangle of giant weeds.

Three boys and Triggot flopped onto the rank grass and stared with the others at the ragged, tumbled ruins of what once must have been a glory. One tower remained and three walls, now roofless. They stood stark against the brightening horizon. No one moved. Even the two boys in the cart did not get out.

"Friends," said Tegonec at last, "I will go and explore what looks now to be abandoned. But who knows what might still lurk in its cellars? Roland will come with me." He released the wolf from the cart. "I expect you all to wait patiently."

"I'll go, too," said Triggot. Tegonec did not argue with him. The boy, like everyone, would have to take his chances.

So the three of them walked the rutted road that led very soon onto the cobblestones of the inner courtyard.

Tegonec let out his breath in a long hiss. "Whoever attacked this estate was efficient, to say the least!"

Spikes of burned wood that must have been a balcony still held to the remaining walls, and huge holes in the stonework revealed the land beyond as though a monster had battered through it. Seeing nothing but a few crows strutting the fragments of parapets, Tegonec stepped through one of the openings in the wall, Roland and Triggot close behind.

There before them, instead of an enemy, were two women, one dressed in pink, the other in gray, one young, the other old, both stooping over, pulling up the weeds that grew among the carrot tops.

"Good morning, ladies," said Tegonec, though he believed them to be peasants. "May I speak to the chatelaine of this residence?"

The younger one smiled. "How lovely to hear this poor ruin described with such courtesy. I am the lady of the house, what's left of it."

Tegonec bowed. He realized now from the delicacy of her speech that she was indeed a lady. "We are aware of trespassing," he continued, "and pray to be excused. But we beg shelter of you, at least until tomorrow. That will give my companions time to rest."

"Certainly, though our hospitality is limited by our poverty. I am the Countess Philomele, and this is my dear friend, Meg. We live here alone."

"How do you live?" asked Tegonec.

"By raising what you see before you—carrots, cauliflowers, onions, apples in season, and peaches."

Tegonec suddenly felt completely at home. "Then we can help you. Crops are my livelihood, too. We can join our trades."

"Your assistance is much needed, but I cannot pay you."

"Yes, you can, madame."

"How?" interposed Meg. "We have only enough to buy wine for our digestion and flour for our bread."

"Yes," added Philomele, "we've not had a taste of sugar in a year, since my husband was killed in battle and his enemies left my castle as you see it now."

"We number more," said Tegonec, "than what you see before you. I have a cartful of helpers, five in all. Add Triggot here and Roland, and you'll head a company of eight. Your welcome would be our reward."

"And if we all work hard, very hard," said Triggot, speaking for the first time, his gaze never leaving the clear beauty of the countess's face, "there should be enough for all."

The countess looked at each of those before her, her glance tender and accepting, but she looked longest at the wolf, from his great gray head to the tip of his long tail. What she saw made her smile. "But you spoke of eight," she said. "Where are the others?"

"Triggot," said Tegonec, "go fetch our orphans."

Together the boy and Roland raced for the border of trees. In three minutes they could be seen pulling the cart, the two boys still able to walk hanging on to its sides, the other three squeezed into a kind of bundle with arms and legs protruding.

Philomele didn't wait for them to enter the courtyard but ran to meet them. "What lovely faces to begin a new morning!" she cried, and laying her hand on the tip end of a shaft, she walked into the ruins with them.

Meg grinned to see her mistress so pleased. She thrust her arms into the cart and hoisted the one who seemed the puniest up and out. Triggot tugged at another, and Tegonec the last. They lined up in front of Philomele and Meg.

For an instant a drift of sadness shadowed the two women. Except for Triggot, these were children destined to die, their having been born at all an accident quickly corrected by hunger and neglect.

"Food first, then baths," said the countess. "Then hugs all around! While you take turns washing in the big tub in the kitchen, Meg will boil your clothes and put them to dry. Then you shall sleep in my big bed."

After soup, bread, and an apple each, Tegonec, Triggot, and Roland watched the two women encouraging the five boys as they soaped themselves, too tired even to splash much when immersed in the tub; and then, looking like bony white specters in their new cleanness, they hopped into the countess's wide featherbed and snuggled like cubs into its softness.

"They're quite accustomed to sleeping on straw," said Tegonec.

"I'm sure of it," said Philomele, "but this once won't spoil them—certainly not after what their life must have been before."

Sitting down on the cracked marble bench that was surrounded by a hedge of briar roses, she urged Tegonec to tell of his meeting with these children. While he talked, Triggot and the wolf went into the near meadow and lay down in the grasses, Triggot's one hand shading his eyes, the other patting Roland.

When Tegonec had finished, having included the presence of the wolf, the two sat tranquil in the morning sunlight. Then Philomele, gazing at Triggot and Roland, both of them dozing as though drugged by the scattering of scarlet poppies that laced the field, said, "But why do you harness him? Is he not a friend?"

"He ate my donkey. Therefore he must take the donkey's place."

"Then he is your slave?" Her tones held more of astonishment than censure.

Tegonec was jolted by this judgment. Had he been less than honorable toward Roland? Did it feed his pride and make him neglectful of the wolf's own welfare? He remembered the scene just before the christening, what the wolf had told him. "I must not be deprived of my nature." Had he, Tegonec, wished to re-create Roland, weaken him, make him a servant, a being inferior to himself? Then he remembered his own vision of himself, a spirit strong enough to tame the most wild, someone who should be recognized for this supernatural gift. But now this woman was, however unintentionally, accusing him of desiring a slave.

He called to Triggot to come nearer, to bring Roland with him. The boy obeyed immediately.

"Please tell him to come to me," said Philomele gently. "See how his coat has been bloodied by thorns and there are burrs in his ears."

Tegonec expected the wolf to withdraw, but instead he came to stand beside the countess, who wasted no time in plucking out the burrs, inspecting his footpads for slivers, and finally taking a little white comb from the bag that hung from her belt and starting to separate the tangles in his fur.

"Look!" exclaimed Triggot, his grin almost reaching his ears. "Roland's smiling!"

But Tegonec was not.

Chapter Ten

For the first few days the five orphans did absolutely nothing but sit and stare, eat and sleep. They seemed to be webbed around by the strangeness of these pleasures.

"Let them be," said the countess, as she, Meg, Tegonec, and Triggot worked the vegetable garden. "They'll come around, and I'd not be surprised if one day they are managing my affairs for me."

Everyone but Meg laughed at the idea. She was too busy superintending the lives of the five.

All went well until one hot Saturday in the marketplace. Philomele was taking a brief rest on her stool beside their booth, while Triggot was guardian of the cashbox and the filling of it. Roland had gone down to the nearby river for a drink, and Tegonec was buying flour. So only Philomele heard the three hulking men just behind the booth, plotting to raid her property.

"I tell you it'll be as easy as plucking a dead chicken. Just the two women run the farm, and with them out of the way we'll find their treasure easy," one of them was saying.

"I'll knock them over with one blow," said the second.

The third snorted. "No need for that. Order them off with a shout."

"I see she's collected a man with her today."

"So? He's brittle. Break like a twig."

"Tonight, then?"

"Tonight."

Philomele said nothing of this oncoming disaster until the first touch of dusk closed the market and they were well on their way to the chateau. And as she told them of the plot, her eyes betrayed tears.

"Is it true?" asked Tegonec. "Is there a treasure?"

"Certainly not. The people hereabout live on legends." Then she added, "We must leave before they come."

There was a brief silence as each one digested this terrible news. Then Tegonec spoke. "No. We will not retreat."

"But we are so few," said the countess.

"There are eight of us," corrected Tegonec.

"You mean the children, too?"

"To be sure. Have you stout sticks for all of us?"

"No. But that can be remedied."

And so it was, as soon as they were gathered together.

Tegonec sent the five boys into the woods, and it was only ten minutes before they came running back, armed with branches that they soon shaped into clubs.

While they were gone, Meg and Triggot were whittling points on sticks and the countess stacked her entire collection of pots and pans in one heap.

"Now, Triggot," said Tegonec, "you help the boys pound the cabbages onto the sticks. We want the effect of many men. It will be dark enough so that the cabbage heads will deceive them. Then give each one a pan to bang—but no practicing. Our attackers might hear us."

He stationed Meg on the one parapet. "You are our lookout. The minute you see them coming, strike your kettle—hard."

The enemy, still under cover of the forest, were bragging in such loud voices that they stilled the birds.

"Nobody but two women and a man who looks like a root."

"Simple as splitting an apple with an axe."

Tegonec, hearing the tones but not the words, wished that Fanfare were there to kick and bite them and bray their ears deaf. How very long it seemed since the donkey went to rest in the wolf's belly!

But these thoughts soon dispersed. The three men were

just about to reach the wall and enter the courtyard when a din like twenty demons burst from the parapet, accompanied by curses that rained ill luck down on their shoulders.

Then, rising above the rear wall, appeared a series of giant silhouettes brandishing sticks to the cacophony of a thunderous crashing of pots and pans, and above it all the booming voice of Tegonec shouting, "Bring up the catapult! Pour the oil! Alert the archers!"

The three halted as though stunned. But what sent them fleeing down the road was the monster that nipped at their heels, snarling and jumping, such a whirl of movement as to be nearly invisible. They scattered like rabbits as they reached the first trees.

Roland trotted back to the chateau and received pats all around as the boys tossed the cabbage heads into the air. And Meg, thoroughly pleased with her part in the defense, gathered up the pots and returned them to the kitchen. Then she called in the company. "I must have baked blueberry cakes for just such a celebration," she said, smiling at each one in turn. She beckoned them to seat themselves at the long table. Philomele poured out small glasses of cider, and Triggot distributed them.

When all were settled—even a place for Roland had been made between Triggot and an orphan—Tegonec raised his glass and said, "A toast to each and every one! This night will begin the Legend of the Chateau Philomele and the Beasts, the dreadsome beasts who guard her. I know these people." He turned to address the countess. "You will never be bothered again, except perhaps by small children who are curious and too young to be afraid. And those you can invite in for bread and jam."

Philomele laughingly raised her glass to Tegonec. "We are grateful to you, to you and your wolf." She paused. "Dear Roland," she murmured, and was certain that he returned her smile.

Later that night before the hearth fire, and after many more congratulations, Tegonec diminished their common joyousness. "Dear Countess, we must be off, Roland and I."

Philomele's breath caught in her throat. "But why? Why not stay with us? I don't understand."

"You have enough of a family now."

The five boys, cross-legged on the hearthstones, looked up at the countess and, as if directed, grinned their acceptance of her. She leaned down and patted each one on the top of his head. "You will be happy here then?" she asked them.

Three nodded vehemently. The other two chorused a fervent "Oh, yes!"

Only Triggot said nothing. He had moved to the back of the room where Roland lay watching.

Philomele did not forget him, but realized he had need of this withdrawal.

Tegonec rose from the bench where he had been sitting and first embraced the startled Meg. She hugged him back. He shook each of the five orphans by the hand and said, "You will take good care of your guardians and work hard." Their response was a unanimous "Yes, sir!"

Since Triggot did not come forward, Tegonec merely

waved his farewell of him and beckoned to Roland. Then he turned to the countess, and with a very low bow, as to a queen, he kissed her hand. This time he did not speak, nor did she, but their faces reflected, one to the other, a deep sadness. Tegonec walked out of the ruins and down the grassy alley without a single backward glance, pulling the cart behind him.

When he reached the high road, Roland joined him.

"I wasn't sure you would come," said Tegonec to the wolf.

"Nor was I" was the wolf's reply.

A small shadow emerged from behind a nearby tree trunk and stepped full into the moonlight. It was Triggot.

"Surprised?" he said. "Never intended to stay behind and play nursemaid to those little ones. Not my role, not in this life." His bravado was somewhat shaky.

"My life is chancy," said Tegonec. "Yours would be less so with the countess."

Triggot shrugged and explained nothing.

"All right. You may come with me. As to Roland—" Tegonec paused, his voice doubtful. "He has his choice to make, too."

Roland did not speak again, and Tegonec guessed his silence was caused by the presence of Triggot. Their speech together had, up to now, been secret. But the wolf did, in another way, reply. He stepped into the harness of the cart and waited to be buckled in.

"For my sake?" Tegonec asked, but Roland only started forward.

CHAPTER ELEVEN

*T*he next evening as Tegonec was dozing by the fire, the day having been long with walking, his mind awakened though he did not open his eyes. Triggot, a few yards off on the other side of the flames, seemed to be talking to himself.

Tegonec was a little surprised. The boy had spoken during the day only when spoken to and seemed to be in some distant place. Perhaps he regretted not staying with the countess and Meg.

At first the words were blurred, and then, as the gentle night breeze shifted, they came clear.

"I used to imagine what it was like," the boy was saying, "to have a father and mother, but then I gave that up. I didn't know the details well enough to make it seem real, even if it was only in my head."

"I understand" came a reply.

Tegonec lifted his head and looked. Triggot was not talking to himself but to someone! The someone was Roland. But how could this be? Roland had never communicated with anyone but himself, Tegonec. He remained as if asleep and listened.

"I believe you do," Triggot said. "You're a very sympathetic person."

A deep kind of rumble came from the wolf's stomach. He was laughing. "First time I've been called a person. Can't say as my costume is very convincing."

Tegonec saw Triggot stroke the animal between his ears. "I think your costume is beautiful. And how warm it must be on winter nights!"

"Yes," responded Roland, his voice elongating the word as in a dream, "even a hollow in the snow is a shelter with such an overcoat."

"You sound sad," said the boy.

"I am not the happiest of wolves," said Roland, trying to lighten his voice.

At that moment a far-off howling made him prick up his ears. "Listen, Triggot, listen."

The distant voice was answered by another and then another. When silence returned, Triggot whispered, "Is it one of your family, a brother maybe, even an uncle or, best of all, your mother?"

Roland smiled at the boy's eagerness. "They would be cousins, surely." He began to prowl restlessly, making a circle around Triggot.

"You wish to follow the calls, don't you?" asked Triggot.

"Yes. But what of Tegonec? Who will pull the cart?"

Triggot hopped to his feet. "That's not a problem! I will pull it when it is empty and Tegonec when it's full."

Tegonec tensed but he did not move. A strange confusion bubbled inside him. How was it not only that the boy and the wolf could talk to one another but that the alliance between them was so strong, as strong as though they had been together for many months? And now Roland was about to desert him, his master?

He quieted his thoughts and listened again.

"Do you truly believe that would work?" Roland was asking.

"But you would come back, wouldn't you?" said Triggot, the sadness as if transferred from the wolf to himself.

"Someday. To see if all is well with my master."

Tegonec was slightly comforted by the wolf's words.

"You see," continued Roland, "I ate his donkey. I am guilty. I owe him my strength."

Triggot sighed. The idea of anyone rejoining a family was

too powerful. He was deaf to the wolf's statement of obligation.

"I must leave before he wakes," said Roland. "Otherwise I could not go." He looked for a moment at Tegonec's long form and then vanished in among the trees.

Triggot walked to Tegonec's side of the fire, and Tegonec, seeing him come, closed his eyes tight and pretended sleep.

The boy lay down on the ground at the man's feet, resting his back against the soles of his shoes, and slept.

His sleep was uneasy, because he had determined to be up before Tegonec so that he could explain the absence of Roland. But the first shafts of sunlight had already slanted through the tree branches as he sat up and saw Tegonec frying a pan full of beans over the embers of the bonfire.

"Good morning, sir," he began. "Last night I had a talk with—"

"Yes, I know," said Tegonec, stirring the coals. "You will be pulling the cart when it is empty."

"Then you heard us!" the boy exclaimed.

Tegonec nodded but did not turn his face toward Triggot.

There was no further speech between them as they ate and then, having drunk from a stream, started toward the nearest farm. There they collected a load of apples to be transported to a town ten kilometers away with instructions to return with three sacks of wheat.

Triggot did his part, even to buying the grain after the apples were unloaded. But it had been a melancholy day, and the gray mood that had cloaked Tegonec from its start deepened as he leaned forward, straining against the weight of the cart, on the road back.

And that evening, after the boy had built and lighted their evening fire, Tegonec refused the bread and cheese of their supper, saying he was too tired to eat. Triggot knew then that tomorrow must be better, and again he waited until the man was asleep and curled up at his feet like a faithful hound.

Chapter Twelve

*T*riggot woke to the sound of Tegonec's small groans. He watched between half-closed lids as the tall man tried to exercise the stiffness from his body, but when he slumped down on a rock, his head in his hands, Triggot knew that the hurting was not only in his joints.

The boy replenished the fire and divided what was left of the loaf of bread, folding his share of the cheese in with Tegonec's. "You know, sir, you have never told me about your home. Since I have never had one, I would appreciate hearing of yours."

Tegonec seemed to revive as he munched his breakfast and thought about his cozy little hut. "I'll tell you, then," he said. "Those were happy days. My donkey and me, we had plenty of employment in the province and our Sundays to ourselves. And every evening, after Fanfare was bedded down, I took out my harp and sometimes sang away as much as an hour."

"Where is it now?" asked Triggot, pleased to see Tegonec's cheeks pink.

Tegonec reached into his pocket. "Here, safe and sound. And I have another treasure." He pulled out the square of wood that held the saint's image and held it up for the boy to see.

"But it looks like you!" exclaimed Triggot.

"Does it? Really?" Tegonec rubbed his jaw as if to loosen the words behind it. "I'll tell you a secret. I have sometimes believed that I was destined to join the miracle workers of this world, believed it so hard it seemed real."

"But this image must be a sign!" Triggot cried. "A sort of miracle in itself, your owning it and all. You carry the proof. As for the harp, that's for singing."

For an instant Tegonec's face glowed with pleasure, then became shadowed again. "But if this were so, why would Roland desert me? He is part of the miracle, my taming of him."

"He hasn't deserted you. He went back to his own kind."

Now Tegonec's face reddened. "If he had cared, he would have stayed! Friends are loyal or, if they are not, then the friendship never was! And I was a great fool to give my friendship to a creature, to an ignorant wolf!" Tegonec's anger swelled and he fisted his hands and waved them wildly. "A curse on him—that's what I say and what I mean—a curse on him!"

Triggot did not raise his eyes but looked ruefully at the ground. He seemed suddenly overcome by weariness. Slowly he fastened himself into the harness. "Come, sir," he said. "To stand still is to journey nowhere."

Tegonec followed, still muttering indignantly, and it was not until they were joined by numerous groups of travelers that he returned to himself. Far off they saw the spires of a cathedral.

"Must be quite a town," Triggot ventured.

"The center of the province," said a man dressed in new cloth, his face as shiny as a polished apple.

"But why are all these people going there?" questioned Tegonec. "A fair? A carnival?"

"Those and another matter." The man passed them as if in a hurry.

Just before they reached the walls, Triggot stopped abruptly, braking the cart against the backs of his legs. "I must rest a few minutes," he said.

"Better rest your brain while you're about it," said a rude voice. It came from a very stringy woman in a soiled lace cap and a black wool dress streaked with dust.

"Meaning what?" said Triggot, who had not lost his pertness.

"You don't know? Then make room for the rest of us. Everyone will be trying to guess the answer to the riddle today."

"Riddle?" This from Tegonec.

The woman spat scornfully in the dirt at Tegonec's feet. "Must have come out of a troll's cave since yesterday," she said. "The riddle, you dolts, the riddle the king will ask. And whoever gives the right answer will be made his chief adviser and a prince. Anyone can win."

"And you," said Triggot, set on returning her rudeness. "What do you hope to gain—unless, of course, you aren't a woman at all but a pig in skirts."

The woman aimed a slap at the boy, but Triggot easily sidestepped the blow.

Tegonec was observing the passing crowd, and the longer he looked, the wider his smile. "There can't be much wisdom in these hollow heads," he commented to Triggot as they slowly moved through the gates and became a part of the excitement. "I shall try my luck."

The banners from almost every window, the streamers floating like streaks of a hundred sunsets from the rooftops, the flowers thrown down to the passersby, daubing the cobblestones with color, the finery of the people, jerkins in scarlet, gowns of every hue from white to gold, it all seemed to Triggot and Tegonec as though they were immersed in a whirl of brilliance they could never have even imagined. The

pushing and shoving, the anger and the cursing, that domi-
nated the line already formed to the entry room of the king,
did not mar the hope and the gaiety, the songs of the street
musicians, the agility of the jugglers, and the eloquence of a
stage of players, set up in a corner of the courtyard.

Tegonec had stationed the cart under a willow tree just
outside the main gate, saying, "It will be of no use to a prince,
and that is what I hope to be by tomorrow's sundown."

Triggot did not respond, but he wondered at Tegonec's
confidence and was saddened by the exclusion of himself in
Tegonec's plans to become a prince. But, saying nothing, he
held his hurt within himself.

By nightfall the scene had changed. No one sang but an
old crone who was crazily dribbling water over her head
from the well, and the complaints at the delay in getting to
see the king rose like mosquitoes in the damp air. Fires had
been laid on the paving to keep the contestants warm, and
some were cooking what they had brought with them; but
the colors had been erased with the coming of night, and
even the banners hung limp. But what discouraged the
crowd the most was the constant stream of entrants filing
out of the king's chambers, their heads lowered in
defeat.

"What was asked?" came the question again and again.
"Tell us!"
"What was the riddle?"
There were answering murmurs, but neither Tegonec nor
Triggot could catch them. By this time Tegonec had ad-

vanced to within three paces of the doorway. He was so intent on keeping his place, he hadn't noticed the absence of Triggot. A fistfight had begun in front of him, and three men were knocked out of line. Tegonec, slipping through this gap, stood at last on the threshold of the entrance.

As he stared at the scene within, his mouth dropped open. Lighted torches set into the white columns on each side of the long stone hall illumined the hanging banners above them, and even higher up a gallery ringed with stained-glass windows blazed down such splashes of color that Tegonec imagined the marble floor under his feet to be awash with liquid fire.

A courtier prodded his back. "Don't stand there like a dolt. The examiner is waiting."

Bewildered, Tegonec glanced frantically from right to left, trying to identify this personage among the groups of bejeweled men and women who lined the chamber.

Then there came a voice as cutting as a newly forged sword from the far end, where now Tegonec could make out a golden throne and a small man in scarlet seated between its sculptured arms. But the voice was not that of the crowned one. A very tall man dressed entirely in black except for a medallion—a starburst of diamonds—around his neck, spoke again, and this time Tegonec's mind had cleared sufficiently to make out the words.

"This is becoming very tiresome, milords and ladies, for us all, and since we have questioned, by count, three hundred persons, with no better results than what might have been offered by the denizens of a barnyard, I tender to my liege lord and king that we cancel the contest."

He bowed toward the monarch, who, in a half doze, started awake. "We have an answer then?" said the king, forcing his eyes to open wide.

"No, your majesty. I was merely saying that we are tired and ready for feasting. You will remember that you are presenting us with roast boar tonight, hunted and brought down by your own hand."

The king smiled with satisfaction. Then he bethought himself. "But what of the waiting contestants?"

"One more then, to satisfy your majesty's fine sense of justice?"

At this pause, while the monarch considered his response, Tegonec felt an urgent tugging at his right sleeve. It was Triggot, his narrow face screwed out of shape by his eagerness to speak.

"Get away!" ordered Tegonec. "You've no business here. This is my chance, my only chance to advance in the world."

"But sir, you don't even know the riddle!"

"And you do?" Tegonec, almost throttled by his desire to seize even a small portion of this surrounding glory, seemed to have lost all consciousness of his former fondness for this orphan boy.

"I do, sir. I heard it an hour ago, but I couldn't reach you."

Tegonec noticed now that the boy's shirt was torn half off one shoulder and a bruise was forming on his cheekbone, but even when Triggot added, "I was nearly trampled under twice," Tegonec still felt no touch of compassion for him.

"What then is the riddle?" he said impatiently, still certain that the answer, no matter how difficult, would come to him as by magic.

> "The cold moon changes face and form
> While I rise always full and warm.
> Moon rays light the lovers' way
> But I give strength throughout the day.
> Who am I ?"

Triggot ducked the outflung arm of the man behind Tegonec.

A sudden darkness, as dense as the night around him, blocked Tegonec's mind. His thoughts were as aimless and frantic as trapped rats. He was filled with a sense of his own stupidity as he tried to arrive at an answer. He turned to Triggot. "Help me. But how can you, an ignorant orphan with no schooling? Wait." His face smiled all over. "I have it. The sun, of course."

"No, no! That's too easy," said Triggot. "Everyone is guessing that."

"And I'm no better than the rest, is that it?"

Hearing the beginning of anger in Tegonec's voice, still Triggot dared to suggest. He raised both arms and circled Tegonec's neck, pulling him downward. The man resisted, but could not help hearing what the boy hissed in his ear. "Listen! I have it! I have the solution!"

majesty this distinguished gentleman, so royally dressed, of a lineage beyond compare, excepting yourself, of course."

At this the court's formerly contained amusement burst into circles of laughter that rose to the vaulted ceiling and echoed back again and again.

The examiner flicked an imaginary fleck of dust from Tegonec's shoulder. "Begging your pardon for touching such brilliant apparel," he said.

The courtiers' laughter rang twice as loud.

But the king, who preferred to provide whatever humor was present, was concentrated on having his haunch of boar and soon. "You may ask the riddle," he said.

The examiner winked broadly at the assemblage and with exaggerated courtesy spoke the question.

> "The cold moon changes face and form
> While I rise always full and warm.
> Moon rays light the lovers' way
> But I give strength throughout the day.
> Who am I?"

Tegonec, who through this confusing ordeal had not had the countenance to do more than hang on to Triggot's answer, said it in a voice so faint even the king had to lean forward to hear it. "Bread."

The examiner's tallness seemed to shrink, and he stayed speechless.

Meanwhile Triggot had been thrust back into the restless

throng, and he had no choice but to worm his way free or be crushed. So he didn't hear the cordial greeting of the king or his orders to confer all honor and attention onto this brilliant man who had solved the riddle. Nor did he see the king signal two squires to escort Tegonec to his new apartments and then rise to lead the way into the dining hall.

He waited just inside the outer entrance to the courtyard for a brief while, hoping without much hope that Tegonec would send for him to share his new eminence. But only the night wind spoke to him with a whining in his ears.

The rest of that night, while Triggot curled, shivering, under the shabby blanket on the hard boards of the cart and dreamed he was eating hot turnip soup with leeks, Tegonec tunneled under silken sheets and embroidered quilts, dreaming with a difference. He felt he was being smothered by six coverlets of gold mail that grew heavier and heavier, until at dawn he wrestled his body out from under them and found himself lying on the floor.

Sweating so that his linen nightshirt stuck to his back, Tegonec got up and hurried to the casement window, swallowing the fresh air as if thirsty, staring out into the forested landscape to dispel the nightmare. He heard a loon's long call and was reminded of Roland. Was the wolf stalking a forest like this one or perhaps only strolling, accompanied by his new companions? This thought increased his distress.

After he had slipped on his old, raggedy costume, abandoning the peacock trousers and jacket his valet had set out for him the night before, Tegonec drew the little harp from his coat pocket. But his fingers faltered as he plucked the strings, and he put it away again. As though guided, he next extracted the wooden panel and gazed for an instant at the serene, painted portrait. How could he ever have imagined that this was, miraculously, a likeness of himself?

His cheeks flushed with shame. How blinded had he been with pride, thinking that he might be a saint! That was a journey so distant not even a second lifetime would lead him into the outer boundaries of holiness. No wonder Roland had left him. And Triggot! The boy had given him the gift of all this richness, and there had been not the smallest space in his heart for his welfare. What of him? A wild boar would have shown more concern for such a friend.

Gently he placed the painting on the marble mantel. Someone else should have the privilege of its ownership. Anyone else, even the lowliest serf.

He cautiously made his way down the two flights of stairs, across the great hall, and into the courtyard. No one challenged his going, and the single guard merely jeered at him as he passed. Then, just beyond the ramparts, he saw the cart. He ran toward it, praying for the sight of Triggot, but when he arrived, it was empty and held no trace of the boy. Only the rumpled blanket told Tegonec that Triggot might have slept there. But he was too late.

Desolate, he began to walk, pulling the cart, and when dawn came he sat down on the grassy turf by the side of the road and wept.

CHAPTER FOURTEEN

*H*e felt a touch on his back and, wiping the tears from his cheeks, looked up. A woman, dressed in the coarse cloth of a peasant, was leaning over him. "Can I do anything for you?" she asked.

"Just tell me if you have seen a small boy wandering on the road," Tegonec said. "A very thin boy, but lively."

She shook her head. "There are many strays these days. Who can tell one from the other?"

Tegonec got to his feet and, seeing that the woman was carrying a large sack on her back, offered to haul it for her.

"No, but thank you. I will be leaving the highway now. My farm is just over the next hill. Good-bye and Godspeed." Without a further word she took off through the high weeds that bordered the road.

All that morning Tegonec asked the same question of anyone who would listen. "Have you seen a very small boy named Triggot?" But no one could offer a clue or even a hint of his passing.

When evening came, his legs aching as though someone were prodding his muscles with a skewer, he followed after the last of the travelers, his question unanswered.

At last, alone on the moon-white highway, he felt his strength and his courage come to a halt, and he turned his face toward the dense blackness of the forest on his left. If only he could drown in that darkness! He lay down in the cart and welcomed the cover of night. There would be no one to witness his shame, his betrayal of the boy who had trusted him. But as he closed his eyes, a long, gray shadow paused and then loped off through the trees.

The next day dawned gloom. The sky was streaked with charcoal clouds, and Tegonec's waking moments matched the chill of the whirl of wind that stirred the overhanging leaves. Where could he go? Where could he search for the vanished Triggot?

Then the image of Philomele filled his mind. Maybe, just maybe the boy had returned to where the other orphans had found a home. Without much more hope than he could have stuffed into a walnut shell, he retraced his journey, and just as the evening star appeared over him, he arrived at the ruined castle.

Meg was the first to see him. "Come! Come quickly!" she called, and in an instant all five boys, Philomele following, ran to greet him. Both women hugged him hard. The boys shyly shook hands all around.

"But you look exhausted!" cried the countess. "Meg, serve the soup immediately while I slice the bread. You boys set out the bowls and spoons. Hurry now. Our guest is hungry."

The children scurried to obey as Meg ladled the steaming vegetables into a tureen. In three minutes they were all seated, Tegonec beside the countess. No one spoke until the soup was gone, and then Philomele turned to Tegonec. "What news, dear man?" she asked. "Where are Roland and Triggot? Surely they haven't deserted you!"

Tegonec's throat was so constricted he couldn't speak. He simply shook his head helplessly.

Philomele, sensing his extreme distress, ordered the children to their straw pallets in an upstairs room and, signaling Meg to clear the table, led him to the familiar little chamber off the kitchen. She realized his need for privacy.

"I hope you will be comfortable in your old quarters," she said. "I'll have Meg bring you a coverlet. And now I bid you good night. Sleep well. We will talk in the morning." With that she hurried away.

He flung himself onto the bed, facedown, and tried to

smother his thoughts until at last he drifted into a muddled sleep.

After a first meal of baked apples and steamed oats, Philomele dismissed the five children, sat herself down beside Tegonec, and began mending a ragtag collection of clothing. She waited quietly for Tegonec to speak.

The day was at midmorning before the desperate man, his hands twisted together as tightly as if knotted, forced out the first words. "I betrayed the child and am damned forever."

Gently Philomele drew out the rest of the happening.

"So you see before you," Tegonec concluded, "a being unworthy of life. Triggot may be dead, trampled by the castle crowds, or lying broken on the stones of some lonely place with no one near to hear him." Tegonec covered his face with his hands. "Even Roland recognized my unworthiness and left me. Without Triggot, without Roland, I am only half myself."

Philomele put her arm around his shoulders, and for a very long time they sat thus together. But when Tegonec raised his head and looked into the kindness of her eyes, his own were clouded and unseeing, and she knew that nothing she could do or say would heal him.

At that instant there was a scatter of cries from the forest, and from among the columns of tree trunks the five orphans leaped high, shouting as they came, "I saw him!" "He's in there!"

"Who?" asked Philomele. Meg had come from the kitchen. "The wolf! The wolf!"

"He brought the others!"

The countess caught the leader around the waist to halt his excitement. "What others? Catch your breath, child."

"Look for yourself!" The boy pointed toward the woods.

Philomele gasped. There, in a long line, was a regiment of wolves, their gray bodies splotched black by the spread of leaves above them, the gleaming of their eyes making a string of rubies in the shadows.

"Stay back!" cautioned Tegonec.

Then he saw one of them step forward, raise his head to the sky, and howl. The others howled with him, a chorus of such beauty it stilled every bird and animal in the forest.

Silently, as though erased, the wolves vanished, leaving only one.

"My God!" whispered Tegonec, not quite believing. "Roland!"

He ran across the meadow to the wolf, dropped to his knees, and buried his face in the animal's fur. "Forgive me for not understanding," he said in a muffled voice, "but all is lost. Triggot has disappeared and is not to be found."

Roland spoke as he had always spoken. "Why do you say that?"

"Because I do not deserve to find him. It is a judgment on my folly."

The whole story poured out of him in a rush of words. Roland stood motionless, listening. Then, when Tegonec was done, he placed himself in the traces of the cart and stood expectantly.

Philomele had remained where Tegonec had left her, but rose to her feet as she watched the loving greeting between man and wolf. When she saw Roland go to the cart and Tegonec begin to adjust the harness, she knew her persuasions would be useless.

How quickly the decision to be off had been made! It almost seemed to her as though the two of them had talked the matter over. Hiding her sadness with a smile, she went to them and, instead of attempting to prolong their departure, made only one request. "Play one last song on your harp to keep us joined until you return."

Tegonec looked away from Roland and took the little instrument from his pocket.

> *"I sing a rose,*
> *a flower*
> *that grows with leaf and thorn*
> *so gently green,*
> *it constant shows*
> *in every hour*
> *your beauty born*
> *a Queen."*

The song wrapped them around with silence, and in that silence Philomele kissed Tegonec on both cheeks, bent to kiss the wolf between his ears, and then stood quiet in a gesture of farewell. And while she and Meg and the five children watched the two travelers grow smaller and smaller as they entered the distance until they were only inches high, little sighs came from their mouths. Would any of them ever see Tegonec and Roland again?

Chapter Fifteen

The next day Roland began to recognize trees and fields. "But why are we retracing our journey?" he finally asked Tegonec, who had been brooding ever since they had left the countess and her family.

"It's our only chance. The woman at the orphanage may have had word of him."

Roland was astonished but kept his feelings to himself. "That is the last place Triggot would return to," he said mildly. "One doesn't repeat unhappiness, unless by accident."

Tegonec turned from the wolf. His voice was low. "I don't know where else to ask," he said.

Roland did not question him further but kept to his side, occasionally rubbing against his leg as they walked.

Afternoon had descended when they arrived at the entrance of the orphanage. A sullen, yellowed sky hung over them and the air was heavy with a stale, sulfurous smell.

"I don't believe it!" exclaimed Tegonec as he scanned the fire-blackened walls, the broken windows, the front door that was ajar, ushering them into the emptiness of the building. Cobwebs smeared their faces as they explored the deserted halls, peering occasionally into a room that was strewn with singed books and papers. Everything stank of scorch. It was as though a storm had raged through the corridors, sucking up the litter and then whirling it back again any which way. Rat and mouse droppings peppered the floors, and dirt filled the corners.

Suddenly Tegonec ran as fast as he could, sometimes stumbling, until he was again outside of this ruin. Roland followed. There had been a wildness in Tegonec's exit, and the man did not stop but dashed down the road as though he had forgotten the wolf entirely.

Roland kept well behind until at last Tegonec slowed to a walk and then sat abruptly down on the ledge of a ditch.

The wolf saw the man so encased in despair, he knew he must say something, anything sensible to bring him out of it. "We must return for the cart," he said.

Tegonec nodded, but his eyes were dulled and his feet

dragged as they made their way back to the abandoned school. As if in sleep he fastened the harness around the wolf's body. When the last buckle was in place, his vision cleared and he stared intently at Roland. "Why do you stay with me?" he asked in a thick voice. "Why don't you seize your freedom and run with it?" He reached toward the harness as if to unfasten it.

"No," responded the wolf. "I destroyed your means of gaining a living when I ate your donkey. I owe you my services."

Tegonec shook his head slowly from side to side. "All that is of no importance now. You owe me nothing. It is I who am in debt—to you, to Triggot." He had no sooner uttered the lost boy's name than his face was convulsed with grief.

Roland looked away. "How can you be so sure he is lost to you forever?"

Tegonec breathed deeply. "Should he ever again follow the footprints of the person, the villain, who betrayed him, who stole the answer to the riddle, shoved him aside, and buried his shameful snout in the riches, the promises, the power— all without any thought of sharing with the boy who had given him all this munificence?" Tegonec was shouting now, his face fiery, his arms waving wildly. "I am a swine, a dastardly, selfish swine!"

Roland knew no other way to constrain him, to level off his hysteria. He howled.

Tegonec was so startled, the spate of words stopped. As though the sound that crescendoed and then diminished to nothing had siphoned off Tegonec's desperation, the man fell into a profound quiet. Roland even had to nudge him forward with his nose to start him walking. But which way?

Tegonec spoke as if hearing Roland's question. "There is no way for me to go now but all the way back," and the wolf truly realized that Tegonec believed he would never see Triggot again.

So began a long, dark month. They found small jobs to do, at least big enough to enable them to afford a sack of apples and a daily loaf of bread; and no one would miss the occasional peach or pear they took from an orchard. But none of this could cheer Tegonec, and Roland watched him become thinner and thinner.

At first the wolf would question him, hoping to rouse him from his depression. "Are you trying to match your shadow?" he asked once. The reply was "If that is my fate," and only seemed to plunge Tegonec further into his inner tanglewood. So Roland was grateful when they came at last to the marketplace where they had once been. It was one step nearer Tegonec's homeplace.

They had not long to wait before Tegonec arranged to take five sacks of flour to the monastery where Roland had been christened. But he had no sooner lifted the first sack an inch from the ground when a woman shrieked, "My God and little apples, the beast is back!"

Another took up the cry. "Quick—kill him!"

A butcher started toward the wolf, a blade as long as his arm upraised.

Tegonec shoved the sack aside and, grabbing one of the shafts of the cart, pulled with all the strength he had left, Roland straining to keep up with him. It was ten minutes before they outdistanced the last malediction.

Both of them flopped onto the grass, Tegonec coughing, the wolf's flanks heaving.

When they had recovered, it was Roland who went in search of enough twigs and branches to build a fire; and when it was high he extracted two fat apples from their almost empty sack. Tegonec merely watched, his fingers interlaced as though they were holding him together.

When Roland had eaten—his master had merely tasted his —Tegonec ventured a question. "Why didn't you threaten our attackers as you did that other time?"

"I felt no anger," said Roland. "But," he added, "had they harmed you, I would have struck."

The man looked long at the wolf and his eyes became saddened. "How wrong I was to put myself above you," he said.

Roland smiled and kept silent, but when Tegonec finally fell asleep, he stretched out at the man's feet where Triggot had once chosen to lie.

*A*lthough, as Roland had observed, Tegonec's eyes had searched every roadway, every street, even every open window in the passing towns for the sight of Triggot, he now, in his weakness and sorrow, began to ask again the travelers going in both directions, "Have you seen a very thin boy who calls himself Triggot?"

Over and over the same plea, and often Tegonec would block the person from moving while he repeated the words until he was shunted aside or threatened with a stick or whip. Roland tried to calm him with conversation, but even in the middle of a sentence Tegonec would break off and try again with the next passerby.

The wolf knew they were heading for the monastery and endured the senseless day as best he could until they arrived at its gates. Tegonec was now showing his bones sharply, his face skeletal, his wrists and knees knobbed, his stomach a hollow under his ribs.

At last one afternoon Roland heard the bells, and a few minutes later, at a turning of the road, the high walls of the monastery appeared. He guided the almost unknowing man to the portal and pulled the bell handle with his teeth.

"I will leave you now," said the wolf, "but only until you are well enough to travel again."

Tegonec gazed at him with a kind of puzzled wonderment.

"They forbade me entrance," Roland explained patiently, "and will once more."

Tegonec said nothing. Instead he slowly and awkwardly unbuckled the harness, releasing Roland, and then stood before the entrance, his right hand resting on the wolf's head.

Roland sighed and waited with him.

The monk who opened the gate was very old, his eyes milky as if partially blind. He smiled and said, "You and your dog are welcome. Enter, please."

They followed him to a tiny stone reception room and had scarcely time to look around before a tall, gowned man with a cowl lined in purple silk entered.

Roland felt Tegonec shiver as though in his feebleness afraid. He feared he might faint.

The lines of severity that marked the abbot's face relaxed and he spoke softly. "I am happy you have returned to us, so that we may correct the lack of charity we showed to you upon the last occasion. You were off in such a hurry before we could bid you stay. Now you shall be our guests, and one is no less welcome than the other, man or beast."

The abbot bowed before them. Roland glanced up at Tegonec, expecting him to return the reverence. But though his fear was gone, Tegonec seemed oddly unaware of the honor paid to him. He raised both arms imploringly and asked, "Have you seen a very thin boy who calls himself Triggot?" and fell, unconscious, to the floor.

Three days later the constant care of the monks had returned some of his strength to him. During the first day beef broth had been brought to him hourly, and as he managed to consume it, many delicacies followed on his bedside tray. On this third day Tegonec informed Roland that it was time to move on.

The abbot attempted to persuade him to stay, to become a member of the brotherhood. "You will have a special place among us, and Roland, too, will receive the highest respect."

Tegonec thought back to the days when he would have seized this prestige as owed to him, the man who had tamed a wolf. Now he simply kissed the abbot's ring in farewell, thanked him, and added, "I have done someone a great wrong. I am not worthy."

The abbot ruefully assented and then beckoned to one of

the monks to advance. Tegonec was offered fresh clothing, a wool cloak, and a pair of newly fashioned sandals.

"No," said Tegonec, "I will remain in the covering of my guilt."

The abbot smiled. "You speak as a saint might speak."

At this Tegonec was convulsed by a suffocating explosion of laughter, laughter that was so bitter the wolf clenched his teeth around Tegonec's wrist and pulled him all the way to the gate. He hastened to fit himself between the shafts of the cart and, as soon as Tegonec had strapped him in, set off at a trot, knowing that Tegonec would follow.

But they had not gone three hundred paces before Roland suddenly slid to a halt, almost tilting Tegonec over the cart.

A band of archers, twenty strong, barricaded the highway. Tegonec recognized the coat of arms on their breastplates as belonging to the baron. He and the wolf were immediately surrounded.

"But why would you want us?" protested Tegonec. "We exist at the bottom of the well of poverty and have nothing to give."

"We have been watching for you on the orders of our master," said the leader. "That is all I know. Come. It would be best if you came willingly."

Roland and Tegonec exchanged a look that was a bond of courage and resignation, understood without words, and were marched toward the baron's castle.

CHAPTER SEVENTEEN

Escorted directly into the great hall, both Tegonec and Roland were amazed to see the enormous assembly of the baron's knights, men-at-arms, squires, down to the last assistant groom. And to the baron's right, his wife and children and a whole section of ladies-in-waiting and house servants even to the fifth scullery maid. Tegonec noticed that some seemed out of breath, as though summoned hurriedly.

"They must be expecting a king," Tegonec said to Roland.

His words were relayed up the line of guards and courtiers all the way to the baron.

The baron smiled and rose from his throne. "Not a king," he said, "but perhaps a saint."

Roland nipped Tegonec's ankle so that he wouldn't burst into that dreadful mocking laughter, but he needn't have worried. Tegonec was absorbed in the realization that this mighty reception was for him—for him and for Roland.

"We have heard," continued the baron, "that such a man as yourself has brought a wolf to grace, has converted the wildest beast of all."

Now it was Tegonec's turn to smile. He stooped down and whispered into Roland's ear, "Maybe this is the moment to growl, so that they may witness just how wild you are."

"But enough talk," said the baron. "We are here to do you honor. One must not neglect the holy ones, though they sometimes appear as beggars." He waved his hand toward the left, and immediately six tailors scurried before him, each loaded to his chin with materials of all kinds and colors. They swirled the bolts of cloth open like giant streamers. The court gasped. Never had they seen such a richness. Some pieces were threaded with gold and silver, others sewn into a glitter of gems.

Then a page appeared before Tegonec, holding a golden chain studded with diamonds. It took Tegonec a moment to recognize its use.

He bowed before the baron. "I thank you for these gifts and honors, but we wish only to go as we have come, and my friend has no need of the chain. It would weigh too heavily on his neck."

There was a clamor of protests from the highborn—the others dared not speak—but Tegonec was adamant and was finally allowed to depart, the cart piled high with cheeses, haunches of meat, fruits, and wine.

When they were once more alone on the road, Roland grinned. "I can see the legend grow. Like my stomach after we have sampled all these fine foods. It doesn't take long."

Tegonec's smile was so faint, Roland knew that he was once again immersed in thoughts of Triggot.

That evening, both of them ready to halt for the night, they went into the same forest where they had met so many days and so many happenings ago. Even the cinders of their first fire still remained at the center of the clearing.

Now it was the wolf who joined the almost total silence of the man. He envisioned his attack on the donkey and the terrible anger of Fanfare's master. He heard again the scorching words. "Are you such a craven beast, without conscience, without honor, that you cannot look me in the eye?" Again he felt the pricklings of shame raise the fur at the back of his neck. He watched Tegonec seat himself on a fallen log, his hands between his knees, his head downcast.

To escape his sadness, Roland busied himself in gathering small branches and stacking them for a bonfire. Tegonec roused himself sufficiently to light it and then sank back into his reverie.

"Do you miss Fanfare still?" Roland asked from deep in his throat.

Tegonec raised his head and gazed for a moment that seemed ten to the wolf. "No," he said. "He is you and you are he, two in one."

Roland sat down in astonishment. "You mean because I ate him?" He was aware of the stupidity of his question as he received Tegonec's reply, not words at all, but a look filled with love. The wolf turned his body toward the darkness of the trees and slipped into their shelter, and from a concealing distance howled once, then twice.

Tegonec got quickly to his feet and followed the sound, and as he went he stubbed his right foot against something sticking up from the ground. He leaned over to pick it up. The axe, the very same axe he had flung at the wolf. And when he found Roland, he shifted the axe from his right hand to his left and stroked the wolf between his ears.

There was no need for talk that night.

CHAPTER EIGHTEEN

*T*he next day Tegonec wished to travel rapidly and reach his home before nightfall. But his pace became slower and slower the nearer they came, and Roland knew that it was not entirely owing to weariness but to Tegonec's dread of the emptiness he would find there. The moon had reappeared before they sighted the little path that led to the end of their journey.

Just before the very instant when the hut would become

visible, Tegonec stopped in his tracks. "I can't," he said in a voice that was not quite his own. "I just can't. I must go on and on and on until I find Triggot."

"And if you never find him?" asked Roland, knowing that Tegonec must confront the truth.

"Then I will keep on looking until I drop."

The wolf had advanced almost to the end of the path. "But the door is open!" he exclaimed, desperate to change Tegonec's decision, no matter how. "Perhaps the forest creatures have taken it over."

"Then let them have it." Tegonec was already in retreat.

Roland sniffed the air. "A fire has been lighted, and there is a smell of stew coming from the house!"

"May they find pleasure in it" was Tegonec's response, and now he was almost out of sight and nearing the forest.

The wolf stuck his head in the crack of the door and broke into a howl that seemed to split the sky. He raced down the path, and someone leaped behind him in a frenzied chase.

Tegonec turned, and suddenly he was seized at the neck, his waist wrapped tightly around, held so close he could hardly breathe.

Tegonec stared at his attacker and then shouted for joy. "Triggot! Triggot! Triggot!"

The boy released him and ran to Roland, hugging him just as hard. "Am I not clever?" he said, so excited he squeaked. "I followed your traces. It was easy when the talk of a miracle began to spread—and you are a miracle, you know, you and Roland." He was dancing on his toes while the wolf ran circles around him in celebration.

Tegonec's delight shifted and his face grew long. "Oh, Triggot, do stop talking nonsense and please, please, forgive me. Forgive what I did, stealing your answer to the riddle and your chance to become a noble, rich forever and respected."

Triggot stood very still for a long moment, and the unshadowed shining of his eyes spoke only of his love for Tegonec.

Accepting this silent gift, Tegonec smiled for the first time in many, many days, and so broadly that Roland found himself smiling, too.

"But how did you know the answer was 'bread'?" Tegonec asked.

"One of my jobs at the orphanage was to take the loaves from the oven each morning at four, before dawn. Under the light of that same cold moon I watched the bread rise, so why would I not guess the riddle?" He snapped his fingers. "Besides, who wants to be a noble in this world? I'd rather dance a jig on the floor of your house. Come, I'll show you how it's done."

He led the way inside. "Take out your harp and give us a lively tune."

Tegonec, hardly knowing what he was playing, obeyed, and soon Triggot, partnered by the wolf, was hopping to his music; and like the dust from the earthen floor, happiness rose around them in a golden cloud.

JULIA CUNNINGHAM

is one of the most highly praised and well-loved children's book authors of our time. Her novels have won wide acclaim and many distinguished honors since the publication of *Macaroon*, her first book, in 1962. *Dorp Dead!*, published in 1965, is now considered a modern classic. In 1973, *The Treasure Is the Rose* was a National Book Award finalist, and then *Come to the Edge* won the Christopher Award in 1977. *Flight of the Sparrow* is her most recent novel for Pantheon Books.

Born in Spokane, Washington, Ms. Cunningham has traveled widely and now lives in Santa Barbara, California.